MW00794876

BENZION FIRER

The Twins

a novel

TRANSLATED FROM THE HEBREW BY ❧ *Bracha Slae*

Special Textbook Edition
with Study Guide
by Yitzchak Kasnett, M.S.

FELDHEIM PUBLISHERS *Jerusalem & New York*

Originally published in Hebrew
as *haTe'omim*

Other Feldheim books by the author:
  Saadiah Weissman
  The Long Journey Home

First published 1981
Special Textbook Edition with Study Guide 1987
ISBN 0-87306-279-5 Copyright © 1981 and 1987 by
Feldheim Publishers Ltd.
All rights reserved

Philipp Feldheim Inc.
200 Airport Executive Park
Spring Valley, NY 10977

Feldheim Publishers Ltd.
POB 6525/Jerusalem, Israel

Printed in Israel

My town

Once there was a town
which prayed a fervent prayer.
"Let my name be remembered," it asked.
"That is all I desire."

It told a well known story.
"I was the ancient home
of a holy and honored community.
I lived a rich, full Jewish life,
surrounded by my people.
My fame reached high places,
and my name was spoken with reverence and esteem,
for men of great stature lived within my walls.

"Men like the famous Reb Mendele,
his disciple Reb Hirsch,
and his son Reb Yosef.
Where are their graves today?
Any scholar will tell you my name
and then add,
'May their merit be a blessing to protect us.'

"Even the unlearned in my midst
were full of *mitzvoth*
as the pomegranate is full of seeds.
They bore the title 'Jew' with pride,
waiting impatiently for the Redemption.

"I loved all my sons—
the learned and the simple,
the great and the small.
I rejoiced in their joys
and was elated at their happiness.
I shared their suffering
and was stricken by their sorrows.

"My bitter end is well known.
In days of darkness,
a wild, barbaric people
ensnared my sons,
and with neither logic nor reason,
killed them all.
Young and old; suckling child and tiny babe;
men, women and children;
all were choked in the chambers of death
as the forces of evil
strove to exterminate
the people of Israel.

"When my sons disappeared,
I too vanished from the map,
my hopes dashed, my prayers unanswered.

"And now, my one remaining desire
is to be remembered.
With outstretched hands I plead:
Let my name be not forgotten!"

Upon hearing this plea, I was filled with anguish.
Would that I could fulfill it! —
but I cannot
for the history of my town is unknown to me.
Her years were already full without number
when I was just a boy;
her story was long in telling
before ever I felt her charm.
And when the Holocaust descended,
I was no longer there.
Before the slaughter began
I had been taken far away.
"I cannot fulfill your request," I wept,
and my town was silenced and sad.
But suddenly, her strength renewed,
she said,
"There is power in man's will,
and that which man truly wills
can be done!

"I have heard of your story — *The Twins*.
It is a tale of two orphans, brother and sister,
caught in the web of the Great Destruction.
Every Jewish town shared in its black devastation;
disaster and courage were equally mine.
Mention me in your story,
and I too shall be remembered.

"My claim upon you is a strong one.
For eighteen years, your father of blessed memory
was Rabbi here within my gates
and now his bones lie resting
in the ground beneath my feet.
You followed in his footsteps and filled his place,
teaching my people the Torah and its commandments.
Who then can I turn to if not you?"

"It is all true," I cry.
"And the story I have written
is your story too.
Let it therefore be a remembrance for you,
a sign that you are not forgotten."

And so, dear readers,
know ye all and remember,
the name of my beloved town was

    RIMANOV

May her memory be blessed.

Benzion Firer

Nir Galim, 5726

contents

≈§ I ৡ৹ *Twins*

There was nothing out of the ordinary when twins were born to Yudel Glick. After all, his were not the first twins in Nachrovah, a city of several thousand Jewish families. However, as time passed, it was obvious that Yudel's children were unique.

They were brother and sister; Yudel called his son Chaim and his daughter Brachah. These names were special; they were not just picked from a book. Yudel chose them because they were the names of his father and mother who had passed away so long ago that he didn't even remember what they looked like. His father had served as a soldier in the army of Kaiser Franz Josef of Austria during the First World War. He had left home twenty-two years earlier when Yudel was only three, and he had never returned. Yudel's mother waited patiently for her husband year after year after year, until tired of waiting, she departed from this world. Yudel was sent from uncle to uncle, from his father's side to his mother's side, from his mother's side to his father's side and back again, until he finally grew up.

His family were all faithful, observant Jews, *chassidim*, although not necessarily of the same *rebbe*. Yudel, however, was outstanding. He was a *talmid chacham* and an enthusiastic *chassid,* and he was beloved by all for both his scholarliness and his *chassiduth.*

It was only a year earlier that Yudel had come to Nachrovah. His father-in-law, Reb Yisrael Reichman, was a learned and wealthy Jew, and Reb Yisrael's only daughter, Esther, was modest, pious, and beautiful. From the time Esther married Yudel, she radiated happiness. The young couple had no financial problems and could enjoy the best of both worlds. Yudel was rich in the world of Torah, and Esther's father was rich in the world of commerce. Thus Torah and wealth were united.

When the twins were infants, not even their parents noticed the great similarity between them. Tiny babies tend to change their appearance from day to day. However, after a while everyone began remarking on the striking resemblance. This resemblance increased as time went on and was the subject of widespread attention. If the twins had both been boys or both been girls, it would have been impossible to tell them apart, for they were like two drops of water. The only apparent difference was in their dress.

When Chaim reached the age of three, Yudel and Esther cut his hair for the first time and made a party in his honor. Then they brought him to the *cheder.* The teacher, seeing Chaim holding his father's hand and Brachah holding her mother's hand, smiled and said, "Are you trying to disprove the teachings of our Rabbis? They praised the Holy One, Blessed be He, and said that when a mortal king coins money, he makes each coin exactly alike. But God who in His greatness created all men in the likeness of Adam, nonetheless saw to it that no one man is exactly like another. Yet your two children are indeed exactly alike!''

Yudel smiled and replied, "Our Rabbis also told us the reason that people are different. Were two men to look alike, one might impersonate the other and steal his house or his wife. But this couldn't happen with a brother and sister."

"You are right, Reb Yudel,'' answered the teacher, savoring his reply.

"Ma'ase avos siman levanim." What happens to a father often happens to his son. Just as Yudel's father had been a victim of war before he reached the age of thirty, so did Yudel become the victim of a war before he reached the age of thirty. For the father, Chaim, it had been World War I; for Yudel it was World War II. Chaim had been drafted into the Kaiser's army, left home, and never returned. His death remained a mystery. But there is no mystery concerning Yudel and his family. Their story is told in the pages of this book.

When the Germans invaded Nachrovah after crossing the Polish border at the end of 1939, they caused great hardship for the Jews in the town. A year and a half later, they enclosed three streets with barbed wire and built a ghetto. Then, large signs announced that all Jews must move into the ghetto. Any Jew found outside after twenty-four hours would be liable for the death penalty.

The first to submit to this decree were the poor, simply because they were more mobile. They had less to lose than the rich, and the threat of death made a strong impression on them. The richer households, however, were in no hurry to follow the order. Some were more fond of their money than of their lives, and some thought that their money would solve any problem. Nor were they as meek as the poorer people.

Reb Yisrael Reichman was among those who were in no hurry to move to the ghetto. "Let's wait and see," he said to himself. "Our Sages said that an evil decree is made to be abolished."

It would be a pity to forsake a house like Reb Reichman's. Most of the things in the house could not be moved because the Germans forbade the transport of furniture to the ghetto. Even if they were permitted to take the furniture, where would he put it? One thousand people could live in these three streets under normal circumstances; now five thousand Jews were being confined there. There was no room for the people, much less their furniture and other belongings. Reb Yisrael remained in his house and didn't move to the ghetto on the appointed day. He locked the door and stayed inside.

Reb Yisrael had a Gentile maid named Maria who had worked for him and his wife Leah for over twenty years. Maria had originally come to their house before Esther was born and later, she had been her nursemaid. Everyone trusted her and thought of her as part of the family. Now — in this time of danger — Reb Yisrael gave Maria the keys to the house and told her that if anyone knocked on the door, she should open it and tell them that the owners of the house had gone to the ghetto.

Reb Yisrael, his wife, Leah, their daughter, Esther, her husband, Yudel, and the twins, Chaim and Brachah, sat in the innermost rooms. Before long, heavy footsteps were heard at the entrance of the house, and a heavy knock was heard on the door. Maria opened the door and found herself face to face with German soldiers, who asked if there were any Jews in the house. But she couldn't understand what they were saying. One soldier knew a little Polish and asked in her native tongue, "Are there any Jews in this house?"

Maria immediately turned and pointed towards the innermost rooms. "In there," she said.

When the Germans entered the rooms and found Reb

Yisrael and his family, their eyes gleamed. With terrifying shouts, they drove the Jews from the house.

Thus, Reb Yisrael and his family arrived in the ghetto, empty-handed and barely alive. Reb Yisrael had lost his gamble. All he had with him was a little money in his coat pocket. He brought even less than those who had practically nothing to bring in the first place

From the very beginning, life in the ghetto was no life at all. Those who had nothing began to starve on the very first day. Those who had money or valuables began to starve a few days or a few weeks later, depending on the amount of wealth they possessed. Reb Yisrael and his family were fortunate enough not to go hungry the first week, but he had to pay whatever price was asked in order to buy bread for his family. By the second week, he had joined the ranks of those who had nothing, and hunger entered his household.

Hunger tends to tease a man and to paint pictures of food before his eyes so that wherever he turns he sees a loaf of bread before him. The whole world seems to revolve around a loaf of bread. So it seems — but only to those who are weak in spirit, not to those who are strong. The latter are also hungry and need bread, but even in times of trouble, they know that man does not live by bread alone. Their need for bread does not blind them; they are still aware of the importance of other things in the world.

Yudel and Esther were strong in spirit. They did not give in. They could be deprived of their bread, but not of their will, and their will was not to lose their share in the World to Come. Bread could be stolen from them, but not their Torah, and as Jews they had to study Torah even when they had no bread. The Torah would help them gather strength until the wicked of the world were destroyed. Without Torah, a Jew would fall into despair.

After several meetings were held in the ghetto, it was decided to organize groups of boys and groups of girls to teach them Torah. Esther was chosen to teach the girls. She was an intelligent woman who had read many books, and few women could compare their education to hers. No one was more worthy of teaching the girls than she. Encouraged by Yudel, Esther agreed to accept the task. She would be a fitting helpmate for him. Both of them would be involved in the same work, since he would teach the boys and she the girls.

Esther's pupils were about nine or ten years old, but Esther frequently took her daughter, Brachah, to the class although she was only six. Brachah was an intelligent girl; she may not have understood everything, but whatever she did grasp would be a blessing for her. But there was another reason Esther took her. She was afraid to leave Brachah at home alone. Jewish children needed the best protection possible from the Nazis. Yudel was too busy to stay home, and the other parents were also away. They spent long hours each day in line, waiting to receive the little food that was offered. Esther was less concerned about Chaim. Although he was the same age as Brachah, he was quicker, more daring, and did not require as much supervision.

One day, Brachah accompanied her mother to the dark schoolroom cellar. It took a few minutes to see inside. There were some shaky benches and a long table made of rough boards, but few books. Esther would tell the girls stories of *kiddush haShem* — of Jews who had been martyred in the past. She taught them prayers and blessings — almost all by heart. Brachah sat quietly and listened. She didn't understand everything, but she understood that she was not to disturb her mother. She sat on the floor in a corner, curled up and withdrawn, waiting for her mother to finish the lesson.

The girls sat and listened attentively to their teacher, Esther. She was a gifted storyteller. As she spoke, the scene would come to life before the eyes of her audience. It fed their souls and made them forget their thirst and their hunger.

Suddenly Esther heard something. She stopped talking for a moment and listened carefully. She wanted to continue teaching so as not to worry her pupils, but she feared that her voice would be heard outside and would lead to trouble. So she continued to speak, but in a whisper. This quietness only served to add suspense to her words. The girls' eyes, burning like hot coals, were glued to Esther's mouth.

The sounds outside grew louder, and the noise increased as it came closer and closer. Esther's heart began to beat faster. She tried to continue talking in order to calm the girls, but she could not hide her own tension. Her voice began to shake. Then, she became silent. Better not to speak at all than to speak in a quaking voice. Esther waved her handkerchief and extinguished the candles burning on her table. Within a few moments harsh knocking was heard at the door. Those inside the cellar held their breath and did not answer. They were all experienced. They knew that crying and pleading would be of no use to them now. They would have no effect on the hard hearts of the Nazi soldiers.

But sometimes silence could fool them, and so they sat in absolute silence.

But this time, it was to no avail. A few kicks at the door with spiked boots, a few knocks with the butts of their rifles, and the door gave way and burst open. In the entrance stood a German soldier, and behind him were two Poles with ribbons on their sleeves and guns in their hands. Esther, who stood at the head of the table opposite the door, ran the length of the cellar and placed herself between the intruders and the girls. She knew that she could not save anyone whom the Nazis wished to hurt, but her sense of responsibility for the girls forced her to place herself between the two. Perhaps this was a mistake on her part. No one who entered the cellar from outside could see anything in the darkness inside for quite a while. Perhaps in the silence, they would have assumed the room empty and would have retraced their footsteps. Now that Esther had acted, they knew the cellar was inhabited. One soldier took a flashlight from his pocket and focused it on Esther's face. She stood proud and upright, her eyes ablaze, deeply afraid, but brave. She too had been influenced by the stories of *kiddush haShem* — of martyrdom — that she had so recently told, and she was ready to act accordingly.

The German looked around at the group of girls and hesitated for a moment. Esther was afraid they would all be arrested, so when the soldier finally turned to her and commanded her to follow him, she rose quickly, before he could change his mind. Now the girls could run home safely, and when danger would threaten her alone, she would figure out what to do. She took her daughter's hand in her own and followed the soldier.

As she passed the street where she lived, little Chaim was standing at the window. He saw his mother following a German soldier. His tiny, thin body trembled at the thought that the soldier was taking his mother to the place where they kill Jews, a place he had often heard of in the conversations of the adults. Quick as an arrow, he ran down the stairs and stood at the gate as his mother walked down the other side of the street. Chaim wanted to scream "Imma!" but he didn't. Perhaps he was so frightened that his voice left him; perhaps he wasn't sure the soldier was really taking his mother away. After all, it could possibly be just a coincidence that his mother was walking behind the soldier, and if he cried "Imma," the soldier would turn around and notice her.

Chaim stood still and didn't call out. Terrified, he watched his mother as she held Brachah's hand. At that moment, Esther stopped for a second, picked Brachah up, and ducked behind the closest gate. The soldier continued walking for a few steps until he realized that the Jewess was no longer following him. He turned around and saw that she had disappeared. He stood still and looked around, his eyes bulging from the strain.

When he looked to the right and saw Chaim, he mistook him for the child who had been with the Jewess. With one jump the soldier entered the gate of the house where Chaim was standing and began to chase after his victim. He opened all the doors of the rooms on the ground level and then went up to the second floor. Nowhere could he find her. He ran crazily downstairs to catch the child and find out where his mother had fled, but now he couldn't find the child either. He thought of asking passers-by, but was ashamed of his failure. After a few minutes of seething anger, the soldier clenched his fist and left.

Those few minutes were centuries to Esther. She had hidden in the stairway opposite her house and couldn't believe that she had been saved. If the soldier had entered the building, he would have found her immediately.

When Chaim told his mother the story, his voice shaking with fear, Esther realized that Chaim had been the angel sent from heaven to rescue her. Although Chaim's clothes were different from Brachah's, the Nazi had not noticed. He had seen only their faces, and so he had been misled. If honest people couldn't differentiate between Brachah and Chaim, how could a person whose sight was distorted by evil tell the difference between them?

∞ 3 ∞ *Deportation*

Life in the ghetto became harder and harder. Worry about food was no longer the only, or the most important, worry. People were afraid for life itself. The Germans no longer had time to wait for them to starve to death. They had begun to murder people whom they did not need. Much slave labor was needed, but only the strongest were chosen for this, and they received work-cards as their payment. The weak, who could not do heavy work, were considered parasites whom the Nazis were loath to support. They were superfluous. Why should people who were of no benefit to the Nazis continue to live? They were sentenced to death.

Since it was not possible to kill everyone at once, anyone without a work-card lived in perpetual fear. At any moment, he might be picked up and sent off to the place of no return.

Yudel had no work-card, but not because he was weak or unable to work. On the contrary, he had a sacred mission which he was not willing to forsake: Yudel taught Torah to innocent, starving Jewish children.

Esther had no complaints over her husband's decision. Although a work-card would undoubtedly have made their family more secure, she could not ask her husband to submit to forced labor in order to receive the card. They both agreed that if everyone worried only about himself, who would worry about those who needed help? And who would worry about the things a work-card could not buy? A work-card could provide a measure of bread and a measure of security, but it could not provide Torah or wisdom, so Yudel remained in the cellar with his pupils, without a work-card. He placed his trust in God and was no more anxious than those who did possess the much coveted cards.

One night, there was no sleep for the Jews of the ghetto. Bitter cries could be heard from many houses as mothers cried for their sons and wives cried for their husbands. People were being taken away. The Nazi messengers of death had come for those who had no work-cards. They loaded them on trucks which transported them to an unknown destination, a place of no return.

The people without cards were like fish caught in a net. There was nowhere to run. The ghetto was enclosed by electrified barbed wire, and no one could leave without permission. It was also very difficult to hide. The messengers of death had a thousand eyes. They could find the smallest hiding place. And there were so many more people than there were places to hide. A precious few did manage to conceal themselves, but the majority sat despondently and waited for a miracle to save them.

Even in those houses where the angels of destruction had not yet arrived, people were aware of what was happening. Anything happening at one end of the street was known to those at the other end, for ghetto houses had many ears. There was no privacy in the ghetto where several families lived in every room, each squeezed into its own tiny floor space. The house where Reb Yisrael Reichman and Yudel Glick and their families lived was also very crowded. It was crowded when everyone stood up and even more crowded when they lay down. There were so many men, women, and children that it was hard to find anyone.

As the Nazis drew nearer to each house, the hearts within held less and less hope of salvation. When the danger was far away there was always the chance that the Nazis would fill their quota of victims before reaching them. But when they came closer, there was little hope left. Even so, people continued to hope against hope until the end. People have an inborn will to live, and this causes them to anticipate all kinds of possible miracles and to keep their hope alive.

In the house where Reb Yisrael Reichman and Yudel Glick lived, there were those with work-cards and those without. Reb Yisrael and Yudel were among the latter. Most rooms contained both kinds of people. Those who held work-cards were both fortunate and unfortunate — fortunate in that their lives were not in danger, but unfortunate in that the jealous eyes of their desperate brothers were fixed on them, as though this tragedy were their fault. Yudel was not jealous of those who had work-cards. He could have had one himself, if he had wanted, and one who has made a choice of his own free will does not blame others for the consequences.

Yudel was also less afraid than the others. The Torah that he taught Jewish children had made him immune to panic and had strengthened his spirit. He couldn't explain why he wasn't afraid. After all, he also wanted to stay alive

Nevertheless, he was not overcome by fear, as were many of the others. Yudel sat silently. Esther, too, did not speak. They were prepared to face the fate from which there was no escape. There was no trick that could save them. They could only wait and see what would happen. Esther's eyes met Yudel's from time to time. They understood each other without uttering a sound. They looked at Chaim and Brachah who were curled up in a corner of the floor in their worn-out, tattered clothes. Tears gathered in Esther's eyes. Yudel pressed his lips together and locked his compassion inside his heart.

The noise drew nearer to their house. A large van stood downstairs, half-full of frightened, degraded human beings, an armed soldier guarding them. When the Nazis entered the house, a tumult arose. Even those who had proper work-cards were unnerved. Seemingly, there was no reason for them to be afraid; nevertheless their hearts were not free of fear. They recalled the Rabbinic saying, "Once the Angel of Death is set loose, he does not distinguish [between men]." It is dangerous to get too close to the Angel of Death, even when he is coming for someone else.

Because of the noise, Chaim and Brachah awoke, lifted up their small heads, and looked with puzzled eyes at the adults. When Esther saw her children sitting up, she said to herself, "The similarity between these two attracts too much attention. If a Nazi catches sight of them, he may be tempted to play games, and the games Nazis play with Jewish children are too cruel." Esther took Chaim's hand and brought him into the next room, appealing to the people there to allow Chaim to remain for a while. The people in the room couldn't understand why she had brought them the boy; but since they pitied this unfortunate woman whose father and husband were both without work-cards (unlike themselves), they complied with her request without asking unnecessary questions.

Chaim felt out of place in this room. He stood bewildered. There was no one his age, and most of the people were unknown to him. He had nothing to do here. It was someone else's room, not his. Why had his mother brought him here? Where was he to go? Where should he sit? In his great bewilderment he stood by the door.

When the Nazis opened the door, they knocked Chaim over. He was hit badly but did not cry. He knew there was no point in crying. He stifled his sobs and didn't make a sound, but he had no strength left to get up. As he didn't get up immediately, one of the Nazis kicked him to the side so as not to block the entrance. Chaim, with his last ounce of strength, pulled himself up from the floor. Another dirty look from the Nazi was enough to send him, shrinking, into one of the corners of the room. The Nazis checked the work-cards of the members of the room, found them all in order, and left.

This particular building had three rooms to the right of the main entrance and three rooms to the left. The Nazis had gone through the first and second rooms to the right. Then they entered the third room where two Jews with no work-cards were taken outside. A few heart-rending sobs accompanied those who left, but immediately stopped. Probably the woman who had cried had fainted. The men who had been taken out tried to explain something while still in the hall, but their captors were not interested. The captives did not submit easily. They had nothing to lose in any case, for you can only die once, so they tried to resist. Finally, the Nazis dragged their victims down to the van and returned to the house to finish their work.

They approached the room of Reb Yisrael Reichman and his son-in-law, Yudel. As they opened the door, Brachah was facing the doorway. When the Nazi who had knocked Chaim down looked at her, he said to his friend, "We were here already," and they left the room.

After the noise died down and they knew that the danger had passed, Esther brought Chaim back to their room. Leah embraced her grandchildren, Chaim and Brachah, and smothered them with kisses. Esther said, "These two children are Good Angels who were sent into this world to bring salvation. And something which has already happened twice will surely happen again when the time is ripe." After a moment of silence, she added, "Please God, may it be this way." Reb Yisrael quickly answered, "Amen." Yudel, who was absorbed in his thoughts, made no reply.

It must be added here that Esther's blessing was not in vain. It came true many years later, although she herself did not live to see it.

◆§ 4 §◆ The Apostate

In Nachrovah there lived a Jew, Yank Shmendrikovitz, who had converted to Catholicism. At his *brith milah* he was named Ya'akov ben Shimon, but when he changed his religion, he also changed his name.

Shimon, Yank's father, had not been an Orthodox Jew. In his youth, when he first heard the news of the Emancipation, he had stroked his beard and exclaimed, "We are saved! Now the Gentiles will no longer murder Jews. The Redemption has come." From that day on, Shimon was one of the "enlightened." He desisted from study of the Oral Law and concentrated on the Written Law, so as not to be different from the Gentiles, for unlike the Oral Law, the Written Law is studied by priests. He also began to study foreign languages, and he trained his hand to write from left to right.

Of course, he was not a Gentile — he was of the Jewish faith — but he thought that if Jews were as similar as possible to Gentiles it would help to unite them. "If Gentiles and Jews dress the same, speak the same language, and read the same books, they will eventually open their hearts to one another. The Gentiles will come to love the Jews."

Of course, when Shimon said "love," he did not mean it literally. He had learned *gemara* in his youth and was familiar with the Talmudic maxim, *Tafasta merubeh, lo tafasta* — "If you grasp for too much, you will retain nothing." One had to be realistic. He knew that the Gentiles would never love the Jews, but it would be good enough for him if they didn't hate them. It would even be good enough if they would only hate them secretly, but not show it openly.

In order to show the Gentiles that he, Shimon *hamaskil*, ("the enlightened"), was willing to meet them halfway, he began to skip certain sections of the prayers. In the *Shemoneh Esreh* (Eighteen Benedictions), he no longer prayed, "Return mercifully to Your city, Jerusalem," or "Let our eyes behold Your merciful return to Zion." He said, "If the Gentiles have given us the Emancipation, we must be just as patriotic as they are. The land where we Jews live now is our homeland. We must love it and not pray for any other land."

Shimon wore a short frock coat, cut off his *peyoth* and trimmed his beard so that it was just like his Polish neighbors'. He considered himself a Pole of the Jewish faith.

He enjoyed studying Hebrew grammar and composing prose in the holy tongue, but he spent most of his time trying to learn foreign languages and reading foreign literature. Not that he was terribly successful in his efforts. Polish words just didn't come out of his mouth as they did from Yanovsky's. There was something in his throat that held them back. Nevertheless, he could exchange a few words with Gentiles when necessary.

If he himself was not overly successful in his efforts, he wanted his only son, Ya'akov, to speak like a Gentile from birth. When Shimon sent Ya'akov to a Polish school, his dream came true. Ya'akov spoke Polish even better than his Gentile friends, and Shimon was extremely proud of him.

"You see?" he said to the Jews of Nachrovah. "When a Jew wants to, he can even speak like a Gentile. It just takes a bit of effort."

The Jews of Nachrovah were busy trying to earn a living and had no time to stand and listen to the opinions of Shimon *hamaskil.* If they did listen, they had no time or patience to answer him back. They kept their distance from him. They felt he was different from them, and somehow this frightened them.

When Ya'akov graduated from elementary school, his father sent him to the Gymnasium. There, Ya'akov did his lessons even on Shabbath. In elementary school, Shimon had asked that his son be excused from classes on that day, but he didn't dare ask for such a thing in the Gymnasium. If the Gentiles were good enough to accept his son as one of their own in the Gymnasium, he wasn't about to make a fool of himself by discussing Jewish things like Shabbath with them. They would only laugh at him.

When Ya'akov finished the Gymnasium and wanted to register at the university, a few Gentiles tried to stop him. But they were unsuccessful, for he was an outstanding student, and they were forced to open their halls of learning to a scholar of his caliber.

Upon Ya'akov's graduation from the university, he decided that his Judaism was a hindrance. Even though he wasn't part of the Jewish community and didn't practice any Jewish customs, the Gentiles considered him a Jew. Ya'akov said to himself, "It is impossible to go on being a Gentile to the Jews and a Jew to the Gentiles, not belonging anywhere. If I am a Gentile to the Jews, I may just as well become a Gentile to the Gentiles." And he converted to Catholicism.

At that time, his father was no longer alive. Ya'akov wondered what his father would have said to him. Would he have been sorry or not? But now he was free to do as he pleased.

After Ya'akov had converted, he married a Catholic woman whose name was Marussa. She was from a wealthy family, had a good education, and a warm heart. Their wedding took place in the Catholic Church according to all the Catholic rules and regulations. Many guests had come from the bride's family, but none from the groom's. A year later, their baby daughter was born and christened Yanka, after her father.

Years passed, and Yank was appointed judge of Nachrovah. This was the reward for his conversion. No Jew had ever been a judge, not in a Jewish town, and certainly not in a Gentile one. But Yank was no longer a Jew and thus could become a judge. The Jews of Nachrovah were displeased. They would have preferred to stay away from Yank and to ignore the existence of an apostate in their midst, but now they couldn't, for he was their judge. They often had occasion to come to court with complicated problems of inheritance, or disputes between neighbors, which ended up in the Polish courts. Of course they would first approach their rabbi to hand down a decision according to the Torah, but there were those who would then appeal to the Polish courts if the rabbi's decision was not in their favor.

And disputes between Jews and Gentiles obviously went to the Gentile courts. No one had asked the Jews of Nachrovah if they wanted Yank Shmendrikovitz to be their judge. Judges were appointed by the government, and the government was run by Gentiles.

Yank Shmendrikovitz was also vice-mayor of the town, in charge of local affairs. The Gentiles had elected him. The Jews had voted for someone else, but the Gentiles were a majority in the town and their votes were decisive. In Jewish affairs Yank was very cautious. He did not want to harm the Jews. He didn't hate them, but he was afraid to stand up for them because the Poles would have said that he was not a good Catholic. Therefore, he took care not to express an opinion.

When the Germans invaded Nachrovah and the Jews' troubles began, Yank was not affected. At first, he was treated like any other Gentile, and he remained at his post. Either the Nazis were unaware that he was a convert, or at that time converts were still considered worthy of being Gentiles. But a short time later, Yank and his family found themselves in great trouble.

One day, after the Nazis had erected the Jewish ghetto, three Gentiles came to Yank's house. One was a German officer and the other two were his Polish assistants. When they asked if this was the residence of Ya'akov Shimeonovitz Yank was so astounded by the question that he could not answer.

Marussa saw that her husband was speechless, so she answered for him, "My husband's name is Yank Shmendrikovitz."

The Poles smiled, and one said, "Where is his certificate of conversion?"

Yank hurried to his desk drawer, and taking out the certificate, which was always close at hand, he thanked God silently that he could prove he was a Gentile. He held out the certificate to the German, who passed it on to an assistant and commanded him to read and translate it into German. The Pole did as he was told.

When he had finished, the German said to Yank, "If so, you were born a Jew and are a Jew now. You must move to the Jewish ghetto."

Yank replied, "On the contrary, this document certifies that I am a Catholic because I converted to Catholicism."

"Once a Jew, always a Jew," the German answered. "Hitler does not permit the Jews to deceive the Christians. Conversion is a Jewish invention to escape the Jewish fate. A Jew remains a Jew even if he has converted to Christianity."

Yank had nothing to say. His face turned white. "I will move to the ghetto with you," said Marussa gently.

"You are a Christian," the Nazi answered, "and you may remain at home."

"Nevertheless," Marussa answered, "I will follow my husband to the ghetto, together with our child."

The Nazi looked at Yanka and said, "The little girl is half-Jewish. She also belongs in the ghetto." That very day, Yank, Marussa, and Yanka moved to the Jewish ghetto.

When Yank entered the gates of the ghetto, a few Jews were standing nearby discussing their troubles. Their faces were serious, their eyes fearful. When they first caught sight of Yank, they made way for him to pass. They may not have liked him, but he did command their respect. As a judge and vice-mayor, he must be treated honorably and according to Polish custom, for he was an apostate and no longer a Jew.

But a moment later, they grasped the irony of the situation. Yank in a Jewish ghetto? What a funny sight! If they hadn't seen it with their own eyes they would never have believed it. One of the group turned to Yank and asked, "Pan Shmendrikovitz, what are you doing here?"

"I was sent here," Yank replied.

"But why?" asked someone else.

"I don't know why myself," said Yank.

"Perhaps it was a mistake," volunteered a third person.

"I certainly think it was a mistake," answered Yank.

"Surely you could have made them understand their mistake, Pan Shmendrikovitz?"

"How I wish I could have made them understand their mistake. The whole world has gone crazy." Thus ended the conversation.

The Jews saw Marussa's weary face, the baby in her arms, and they pitied her. She was not responsible for her husband's actions and should not have had to suffer for them. Yank went his own way, and the Jews went back to discussing their own troubles.

Yank suffered even more in the ghetto than the Jews did. "What do I have in common with Jews?" he asked himself. He neither practiced nor did he know anything about Jewish customs. It was just as if he were born Christian. He was a Catholic through and through. He went to church; he had had a Catholic godfather at his baptism; his Catholic friends had given him many presents and had praised him highly for his courageous act. How could he be called a Jew?

These thoughts gave him no rest. At first he tried to avoid all contact with the Jews. He said to himself, "This is all some kind of insanity. It will pass and everything will be as it was before." Accordingly, he did everything he could so as not to be considered a Jew later. Because he couldn't find an apartment all to himself and was forced to live in a room with several Jewish families, he was brought to despair. He would have been able to tolerate life in the ghetto for a while had he not been together with so many Jews. He erected a wall of silence around himself and talked to no one. Hour after hour he walked the streets, absorbed in his own thoughts.

But after several days, Yank began to realize that his behavior was not wise. Every person must be a part of some group. If the Gentiles were now unwilling to accept him, then he must be friends with whichever Jews were willing to accept him. It was impossible to live in the ghetto and not consider oneself a part of the ghetto. It would be unwise and would gain him nothing. Little by little, Yank began to befriend his neighbors. Not that he considered himself one of them, but he allowed himself to talk to them. Nonetheless, more than once he caught himself saying, "we Jews."

Yank did not work and he had no work-card. He had no need for such card to obtain food, for he had plenty of money and could pay whatever prices were asked. Nor did he think that he was going to stay in the ghetto for long. The Catholic Church would surely intercede in his behalf. They would not permit good Catholics to remain in a Jewish

ghetto. He didn't need the work-card to protect his right to
life, either. Even if his certificate of conversion had not kept
him out of the ghetto, it would certainly keep him from
being sent away to the mysterious place where the Jews were
sent. After all, he was a Catholic.

The night that the Jews without work-cards were
carried away, the Nazis also visited the house where Yank
Shmendrikovitz lived. When they entered Yank's room, he
did not panic, and when they asked for his work-card, he
took his conversion certificate and showed it to them. The
German took the document, examined it carefully and said,
"This is not a work-card."

Yank replied, "It is a certificate stating that I am a
Catholic."

"What is a Catholic doing in the Jewish ghetto?" asked
the German.

"This document shows that I have converted to Christianity," said Yank.

"What were you before that?" asked the German.

"Before that he was Jewish," replied Marussa.

The German laughed and said, "Once a Jew, always a
Jew. If you have no work-card, then you must come with
us!"

Marussa cried out, "Jesus, help us!"

The German looked at her and asked, "What do Jews
have to do with Jesus?"

"I am not Jewish," Marussa cried, showing him her
certificate.

The German asked, "If you are Christian, what are you
doing in the ghetto?"

Marussa pointed at Yank and said, "This is my husband."

"Well," the German answered, "since we are taking your husband, you may leave the ghetto."

They took Yank from the room and left Marussa sobbing. Yank was thrown into a truck already crammed full of Jews, and the Nazis continued their work.

◄§ 5 ∂► *Esther and Marussa*

Esther renewed her teaching in a different place. She did not return to the old cellar, for the Nazis were liable to visit there again. The first time they appeared, a miracle took place, but who could count on a second miracle? One is not permitted to depend on miracles. Esther threw herself more and more into her holy task. She now taught a second group, thirty teenage girls about seventeen or eighteen years old. Esther was not much older herself, but she was wiser. She had been blessed with much wisdom which she gladly shared, and the more she taught, the wiser she became. She was known as an outstanding teacher. The girls were deeply attached to her, and Esther was deeply attached to them. There was great love between them.

She taught Jewish history, where sorrow and hope were intermingled. Sorrow — because Jewish history contains many chapters of blood and tears and much tragedy. Hope — because what was happening now in the ghetto was not new; history was repeating itself.

Esther did not teach from history books. There were many mistakes in the books. Truth and imagination were intertwined, and it was hard to differentiate between them.

Esther taught from memory. True, she did not remember everything by heart. She couldn't say exactly on what date and in which place a certain incident had happened, but she did not attach much importance to the exact date or month or even year. She didn't attach much importance to the place either — it could be a bit to the north or a little to the south, further to the east, or slightly to the west. What was important was an *understanding* of the events which had occurred. She made history live, until it seemed to the girls that each event was happening now, for the first time.

Esther spiced her lessons with the stories of our Sages in the Talmud and Midrash, stories of glory and heroism. For the first time the girls heard of the heroism of other girls their own age, girls who knew how to defend their honor and how to mislead and trap the evil people who tried to ensnare them. The girls' eyes shone. Pride filled their hearts. It was good to be the sisters of such heroines.

Esther also became a mother to her girls. Their natural mothers were so engrossed in worrying about the fate of their daughters in the ghetto that their judgment was clouded, and they had little strength left for understanding their daughters. Esther wasn't worried, so she understood the needs and doubts of each girl. She did all she could for them. If one of the girls was sick, Esther would stand at her bedside and feed her with whatever food she had found. Everyone in the ghetto knew that she obtained much support for her selfless, God-fearing work. She had ways of getting things that no one else could get, both medicine and food. Many people wondered at this and asked how she managed such things. But wondering did not change the facts.

Not all of Esther's girls came from religious homes. One girl, Chavah, who came from a non-observant home, was outstanding in her intelligence and sensitivity. Why had her parents sent her to study with Esther? Because they had drawn nearer to Torah in the ghetto. The hopes they had pinned on the Gentiles were dashed, and there was no longer any reason to imitate them. In the ghetto, they repented and drew closer to God. Before they were sent to the ghetto, they had hidden many things connected with Judaism from Chavah, in order to save her from the suffering of the Jews. "The less she knows about Judaism, the better," they had reasoned. When this failed and they were thrown into the ghetto together with all the other Jews, they changed their minds. Now they wanted their daughter to know everything that other Jews knew. If she was just as Jewish as other Jews, she should know herself. It is not good for a person not to know who he is.

But for three days, Chavah had not come to the cellar. For three days, Esther said to herself, "She must be busy with something else and hasn't had time to come." On the fourth day, Esther went to look for Chavah. She found her lying in bed. Chavah had been sick for three days but was now beginning to feel better. Her father and mother were not home.

Esther sat down at the foot of Chavah's bed and asked what she could do. Chavah said that a doctor had examined her and prescribed a certain medicine, but her parents couldn't find it. They were still out searching for it. Chavah pointed to the long white paper on the shelf above her head, on which the doctor had written the prescription in Polish.

Esther took the prescription, looked at it and said that she would try to find the medicine.

While Esther and Chavah were talking, they heard sighs from the corner of the room. Esther turned her head and saw a young woman lying in bed. Esther questioned Chavah with her eyes, and in a whisper, Chavah told Esther about Marussa. When her husband had been carried off by the Nazis, Marussa's head had begun to reel, and now she was unable to get out of bed. Esther knew the story of the apostate, as did all of Nachrovah, but she knew of his wife only by name. Cautiously, she approached the sick woman's bed and asked how she was feeling. Instead of answering, Marussa sighed.

For three days Marussa had been lying in bed, eating remnants of food. She was pale and weak. There was no one to take care of her. Her husband was gone and the neighbors kept their distance. Marussa understood why her neighbors kept away and did nothing for her. She was an intelligent woman and understood that the Jews were not very fond of the Poles. The Poles had become allies of the Germans and did all they were asked to — and even a little more — to torment the Jews. This angered the Jews greatly. The Germans had robbed the Poles of Poland, yet the Poles were still eager to cooperate with the Germans in tormenting the Jews.

Jews had lived in Poland for more than a thousand years and had helped the Poles build Poland. Now the Poles turned on them and murdered them. Marussa herself had not collaborated with the Nazis. She had suffered from them. Despite his Christianity, they had abducted her husband, thrown him into the ghetto, and sent him to some unknown destination. Nevertheless, the Jews were not fond of Marussa. She too was Polish. Whatever the Poles had done was ascribed to her. If more Poles had been like Marussa, perhaps the Jews would not have blamed her. But most Poles abused the Jews, so the Jews hated all the Poles.

Marussa was an intelligent woman and understood the Jews' feelings. When Esther approached her and asked how she was feeling, Marussa didn't answer. She was sure that this woman didn't know who she was. Were she to find out, she too would keep away. The fact that Esther spoke to her in Polish, not in Yiddish, didn't prove that she knew who she was. Many Jewish women in Poland spoke a foreign language instead of their mother tongue.

When Esther again repeated her question, Marussa understood from her tone of voice that this young woman must know her identity. She must have heard from Chavah. This time she replied and told Esther her story. When she had finished, Esther asked why she didn't leave the ghetto if she had permission to leave. Marussa pointed to a bundle on the right side of her bed, a baby curled up asleep in a pile of clothes. "Whose baby is this?" she asked.

"She is mine," Marussa answered. "Her name is Yanka." Esther understood, and asking no further questions, she promised to bring back food and medicine. It was known that Esther never made promises she could not keep.

Esther returned to Chavah. She sat with her a few more minutes, and then, before getting up to go, she took Chavah's hand and held it for a while. After she let go, she took it again, repeating this a number of times. Esther didn't know what made her do this. Perhaps she had a premonition of some future event. Finally, Esther wished Chavah a speedy recovery and went home.

⊷ 6 ⊷ *The Ordeal*

When the early risers in the ghetto left their houses at sunrise, they saw notices in large print ordering them to appear at a line-up at nine o'clock in the morning in the empty square behind the former site of the synagogue. The synagogue had been burnt down by the Germans with the Poles' assistance, but the square nearby could not be uprooted. It remained in its place. Children and old people were excused from this assembly, the notices said. It was prohibited to bring anything along to the square. The news spread like wildfire throughout the ghetto. Fear filled the air. The ghetto dwellers had learned from experience that no assembly was for their benefit. Each assembly resulted in the deportation of a large — or sometimes huge — number of the assembled to an unknown destination. This destination was dreaded by all. There were many ideas concerning it, but no one dared to speak them aloud.

A tumult arose. People tried to hide, but only a very few succeeded. With every minute the alarm grew, the panic increased. Thousands of human brains were searching for a way out of the trap — in vain. They all knew they could not escape; nevertheless, they tried until the very last minute.

Zero hour was quickly approaching. It was eight o'clock. They had one hour to assemble.

Some people decided to take their children with them. True, the children were not required to attend this torture. But where could they leave them? Sometimes they had to stand in the square for hours. Besides, the children might also bring good luck. A woman with a child or babe in arms might arouse mercy more than a woman alone.

Esther and Yudel were also going to take their children with them, but at the last minute they decided it would not be wise to take them both. They were too identical and might attract the attention of the Nazis, who enjoyed playing cruel games with Jewish children. Only one child should accompany them. Chaim would go with them and Brachah would stay behind. But with whom? Could they leave Brachah with her grandparents? No. Neither Reb Yisrael Reichman nor his wife was old enough to be excused from the assembly. Since every family wanted to stand together so as to know what was happening to their relatives, the grandparents would be standing next to Yudel and Esther; if Brachah stood with them, she would also be near Chaim.

Just then, Esther had an inspiration: Marussa! Marussa would not be at the assembly. She was a Christian and her baby daughter was excused from the line-up because this time all children were excused. She could leave Brachah with Marussa.

When Esther and Brachah entered Marussa's room, Marussa recognized Esther immediately. She lowered her eyes, unable to face Esther. She knew about the assembly and was ashamed that she was privileged to be excused from this dreaded ordeal. Marussa also knew that the Poles were of great help to the Germans at the assemblies, and she was ashamed of this too.

When Esther told Marussa why she had come, Marussa raised her head and looked gratefully at her. Now she need no longer be ashamed of remaining alone in her room while all the ghetto dwellers were forced out of theirs. She would remain not only for her own good, but also to watch over a Jewish child. Her appreciation was apparent as she took Brachah's hand and showered her with kisses.

Esther kissed Brachah on the mouth and left, uttering words of thanks to Marussa. Yudel, Chaim, Reb Yisrael Reichman and his wife, Leah, were waiting outside at the gate. When Esther came out, the five of them went to the assembly.

Thousands of men, women, and children were standing in the square. It was a summer day. The sun had already risen high in the sky and had heated up the air. There was a tense silence. After a little while, a ring of S.S. soldiers with Polish assistants surrounded the square. The dread increased. Reb Yisrael Reichman and his family stood close together. Esther held Chaim's hand. He was still small and he didn't have an adult's understanding, but his fear was as great as that of the adults.

Just then, Poles with official guard bands on their sleeves entered the square. They roughly pushed all the people to the right side of the square. Then they arranged them in rows. The left side of the square was empty. Next, a Nazi with stars on his shoulders and a rubber club in his right hand began to stride up and down the rows. He pulled out a person from here and one from there, and with his cudgel, he motioned to them to go to the left side.

While this was going on, each person was preoccupied with himself, watching only to see if anyone from his own family was being taken. No one paid much attention to the group that was forming on the left. Those from whom a member of the family had been taken were gripped by hysteria and saw nothing. When the S.S. officer had finished his work and left the rows, everyone turned to look at the left side of the square. One hundred frightened young girls, around seventeen or eighteen years old, had been chosen to stand apart. A ring of S.S. officers and Poles surrounded them.

A wave of revulsion passed through the assembled Jews. This was intolerable. Here and there the choking sounds of mothers' cries could be heard. Fists were clenched and unclenched. Something must be done. But what? Older men and women started towards the group of girls. But they were chased away and beaten by rubber clubs.

Feverishly, her eyes burning, Esther searched the group of girls. At one end of the group stood twenty of her students. They were all standing together. They had not been taken from one place but had been drawn together to one place. Esther felt as though fiery coals scorched her heart. She knew that she had only a few seconds in which to act. Soon they would take the girls away. While Esther's eyes were fixed on her students, her eyes met Chavah's. Esther read both despair and a plea in Chavah's eyes. Esther could no longer remain in her place. She removed her hand from Chaim's and moved to her left.

Yudel noticed immediately. He stretched out his hand to take hers and to restrain her, but then he took his hand back. While Esther hurried through the empty space separating the right side from the left, she heard the horror-stricken voice of her father, but she didn't turn her head. She could not allow herself to waver. Any slight hesitation might spoil everything.

Esther stopped a short distance from her students and stood still. When the bodyguards saw a young woman approach deliberately, without the outbursts of those who had preceded her, their curiosity was aroused. One of them asked what she wanted. Esther answered that she wanted to join the group on the left. The guard smirked and said, "As you wish. You are a bit older than the rest, but you may come too."

The circle of guards opened, allowing Esther to join the group. Tears formed in the eyes of Chavah and her friends, tears of happiness. In every tragedy there must be some small reason to rejoice. Esther approached her students and they clung to her. They didn't know if she would be able to save them, but at least it would be easier to bear the terror and dread in their hearts if she was with them.

Esther tried to compose herself but did not succeed. Her heart shook within her. She knew what a great responsibility she had undertaken for the girls' fate. Would she have the necessary strength? Is one permitted to believe in oneself?

The people who watched Esther scorned her. Some thought she had gone out of her mind. Some thought she was a fool who didn't understand what was happening. All thought of her as a poor, unfortunate woman who had sealed her own sad fate.

Soon the order to disperse was given, but no one moved. German guards and Polish assistants pushed their way into the crowd, chasing them out of the square with wild cries and brutal beatings. The square began to empty out, little by little, until the last person was chased away. That person was Yudel. He wanted to see Esther as long as he could. Their eyes met time after time. His eyes full of caresses, Yudel gave his assent to Esther's act. She rejoiced in this; it made things much easier for her. They would share the responsibility together. She was not alone.

After Yudel had been chased out of the square, Esther looked around. The group of girls had formed into several lines, and she entered one of them. They began to march, a ring of guards surrounding them. They left the ghetto and passed the market square where many people were standing about. Today was Sunday, and they had just left church. The Poles watched the strange procession wonderingly.

The girls arrived at the train station where five cars were ready, waiting on the rails. The girls were subdivided into five small groups, about twenty in each group. The Germans had commanded them to divide themselves up, but they didn't interfere with the process. Each girl could choose her own group. Esther and her students comprised one full group. They entered the third car.

One of the guards brought food to the car, good food, the likes of which hadn't been seen in the ghetto for a long time. White bread, butter, sardines and steaming, fragrant coffee. As the guard left the car he told them that the trip would take about five hours. Then he locked the door from the outside, and the train began to move along the tracks.

A deathly silence filled the car. The girls didn't utter a sound. They knew it was now time for their revered teacher to speak. Esther had increased in stature sevenfold. Of her own free will, she had volunteered to share their fate, leaving behind everything dear to her. They felt that they were as precious to her as her own father and mother, children and husband. Who could have imagined such self-sacrifice? Such a thing was beyond their comprehension. She must be an angel, not a human being.

Esther sat on the floor in the center of the car, the girls in a circle around her. She looked into their eyes to see how much fear was in them. To her great joy she saw tranquility instead. Peace of mind is much better at a time like this than fear. Esther began to tell them inspiring stories about outstanding Jewish heroines of the past. They were brave, courageous girls and women who had acquired the right to enter the World to Come in one act. Among others, she told them of the following incident:

Once there were four hundred boys and girls who were taken captive by the Romans for immoral purposes. When they realized what would be demanded of them, they asked each other, "If we drown ourselves at sea, will we merit the World to Come?" The oldest of the group quoted the verse, " 'God has said: From *Bashan* will I return [them]; I will return [them] from the depths of the sea.' *From Bashan will I return* refers to those who are saved from the lion's teeth *(BaSHaN — bein shinei aryeh); I will return [them] from the depths of the sea* refers to those who drown at sea." Upon hearing this, the girls all jumped into the sea. The boys inferred the following lesson from their act: "If girls, who are frequently taken captive (for such purposes) could do such a thing, how much more are we required to do so." And they also jumped into the sea. (*Gittin* 57)

Chavah commented, "How good to have someone great among us to teach us. But what can even a great person do if there is no sea nearby?"

The girls all looked at Chavah, waiting for an answer to the question each one had asked herself. Esther didn't say a word. She pulled out a small bag that had been hidden under her clothing. In it were tiny seeds as white as shrouds. Sighs of relief welled up from the girls' hearts. Some of their faces showed a faint smile of victory. Esther heard the sighs, saw the smiles, and her heart filled with an overwhelming love for her students who would not fail the test. Without a word, Esther gave each girl one seed. Each one held the seed in her right hand as though it were an angel of redemption. They caressed the poison with a tremor of holiness. Joy mixed with fear filled their hearts. Now, if they could muster the strength, evil would have no more control over their lives. Now they alone would control their own lives. They had not felt this way for a long time.

Esther rose from her place, went over to a corner of the car where a bucket of water and a cup stood. She wet her fingers with the water, returned to her place, and began to recite verses of *viduy* — the confession before death. She didn't remember the whole confession of Rabbenu Nissim by heart, but what she did remember was sufficient to purify their hearts. The girls repeated each verse after her. After the confession, they recited *Shema Yisrael* and took upon themselves *ol malchuth shamayim*, the obligation to serve God.

Once again Esther arose, went over to each girl, kissed her on the forehead, and received a kiss in return. Then the girls themselves arose and kissed each other. When all had returned to their places, Esther raised her hand and put the poison in her mouth. All followed her example. Not one hand trembled during this act. Esther said, "You have done well. Avraham Avinu's hand did not tremble either when he took the knife to sacrifice his son Yitzchak."

Then Esther adjusted the kerchief on her head, straightened her dress, and lay down on the floor. Her body was on the floor, but her head was in the lap of one of the girls. All did likewise, each one's head resting in another's lap.

The train's engine went faster. It emitted impatient gusts of air. It sounded as if it wanted to run away from the heroines it carried, but it was unsuccessful. The girls in their car followed behind the engine, as if to say teasingly, "We have arrived at our destination first." When the engine despaired of winning the race it slowed down and finally stopped and was silent. The door to the third car was opened, and the food was found untouched.

The Sokolsky family were Gentiles who did not hate Jews. Mr. Sokolsky was a building contractor who made a good living and led a comfortable life. Until the war he was quite satisfied with his life. He also basked in the honor accorded to his son-in-law, Mr. Shmendrikovitz, who was both judge and assistant mayor. Besides his daughter, Marussa, he also had a son, Stashek, who was a medical student at the University of Cracow. From time to time, Stashek would come home for a visit, and he too added to his father's prestige.

When the Germans threw Mr. Shmendrikovitz into the Jewish ghetto, Mr. Sokolsky's luck changed. Now that the Germans had made it permissible to spill Jewish blood and the Jews were of little value to the Poles, Mr. Sokolsky lost his status. The greatest shame of all was that even Marussa lived in the ghetto, together with all the Jews. Mr. Sokolsky, who had never been an anti-Semite before, now began to love the Jews less. "They always bring trouble," he thought to himself. "Without them, would anything be missing from my life? If Yank Shmendrikovitz had not captured Marussa's heart, this tragedy would never have happened to my family. Wherever there are Jews, there are troubles."

Stashek was even more ashamed than his parents. Mr. and Mrs. Sokolsky were no longer young, and neither were their friends. Older people don't change much from day to day. True, their friends did ridicule them after Yank Shmen-drikovitz had been declared a Jew in every respect and had been thrown into the ghetto, but they did not cut off their ties of friendship. Mr. and Mrs. Sokolsky could also spend most of their time at home and thus retain a quiet dignity.

But Stashek was young, and a young person goes out with friends. Stashek's friends were anti-Semites. They had hated Jews even before the German invasion of Nachrovah; now they hated them seven times more. When Stashek's friends spoke disparagingly of Jews, Stashek would try to remain indifferent, but he did not succeed. He would blush, and his friends would look at him with open derision.

In those days there were two topics of conversation among Stashek's friends. They always began talking about the need to set up an underground to fight the Germans, and they always ended up talking about the German war against the Jews. When they talked about the underground, Stashek would also take part in the discussion, but when the talk turned to the Jews, Stashek felt uncomfortable, as though he too were Jewish and they were talking about him.

The Sokolsky family discussed the matter and decided that Marussa must be persuaded to return home. Once Marussa was out of the ghetto, the Sokolsky family name would no longer be dishonored. Everyone would know that Marussa was no longer Yank's wife, and they would forget their former relationship. Marussa could leave Yanka with Yank, to prove that she had severed all ties with him. Of course they were aware that Marussa would not want to leave Yank, and even if she could be persuaded to leave him, she wouldn't want to leave Yanka, but there was no harm in trying. A drowning man will clutch at any straw.

Who would go to Marussa? Stashek. He would persuade her to lift the shame from her father's house and to correct her mistake. Until now, they had been careful not to visit the ghetto so as not to give people any additional opportunity to look down on them, but now there was no choice. If Stashek would not go, who would?

When Stashek arrived at the ghetto gate, he was allowed to enter. If Jews were allowed to enter, then certainly Poles could do so. But only Poles were allowed to leave. Stashek didn't know where his brother-in-law lived, and he began to question passers-by. But he couldn't get a clear answer. Some pretended not to hear the question, and some heard but answered that they didn't know. Every Pole was suspect to the Jews in the ghetto. No Pole ever came to the ghetto to do anyone a favor, only to cause trouble. Even those who knew Mr. Shmendrikovitz and where he lived hesitated to pass on this information to a Pole. Mr. Shmendrikovitz was indeed an apostate, but the Gentiles considered him a Jew, and the Jews did not wish to cause him harm. Stashek was dressed in a student's uniform, and this increased their suspicion even more, because most Polish students were known to be anti-Semites. Stashek was angry and perplexed. "That's just the way Jews are," he said to himself. "They are not at all polite. They won't even help a man find his sister. They could help but they won't. They won't even cooperate in such a simple thing as telling you where so-and-so lives. They are all liars. The Jews are a strange people. It's no wonder that the Poles don't love them."

Finally Stashek met a Jew who stopped and listened to his request, and since this Jew knew that Mr. Shmendriko-vitz had been taken away by the Germans, he told Stashek where the house was. When Stashek opened the door, he found Marussa. She and her brother stood facing each other, so surprised that they even forgot to smile; they finally recovered and shook hands. Marussa gestured to a shaky chair for Stashek to sit in and asked how her parents were feeling. Stashek gave a noncommittal answer, while examining all corners of the room, which at that hour was empty. He was insulted. His sister was living in a room not fit for any decent human being. Filth like this was possible only with Jews. Everything here was neglected. Neither the floor nor the bedclothing were clean. All the furniture was faded and peeling. "When people say that Jews are not clean," he thought, "there is truth to it."

Stashek paused until he had succeeded in hiding his anger and then he asked, "Where is Yank?"

Marussa lowered her wet eyes and said, "They took him away."

At that reply Stashek could have jumped out of his chair from sheer joy, but he forced himself to sit still. "And where is Yanka?" he asked.

"Yanka went for a walk with Brachah," answered Marussa.

"With whom?" he asked.

Marussa told Stashek about Esther, and Stashek asked.

"What do you think made that Jewess do such a thing?"

Marussa answered, "She probably lost her senses from so much suffering."

"Perhaps she came to her senses and became light-headed," suggested Stashek.

"If you had known her you wouldn't say such a thing," answered Marussa.

Stashek replied, "Even those who think they know them, don't really know them."

"Whom are you calling 'them'?" asked Marussa.

"The Jews," answered Stashek. Marussa looked at him but didn't reply.

Just then, the door opened and Brachah entered, holding Yanka's hand. Stashek picked Yanka up and put her on his knees. Then he pulled a chocolate bar out of his pocket and gave it to her. Marussa took the chocolate away from Yanka and broke it in half. She gave half to Brachah and half to Yanka. Stashek looked at Marussa but said nothing.

Then Stashek put Yanka down, gave her to Brachah, and told the girls to go outside for a while. When they had left, he said to Marussa, "Let's get to the point."

"What point?" she asked.

"To the reason for my visit."

"I thought you came to see me," said Marussa.

"I did, but I also came to ask why you don't leave," said Stashek. "If Yank is no longer here, why are you staying?"

Marussa replied, "I did want to leave already, but I'm afraid that they won't let me take Yanka out."

"I'll take Yanka," said Stashek. "If they see her in my

arms they won't dare to stop me. She even looks like me. The guards at the ghetto gate will think she's mine."

"But," asked Marussa, "what will happen to Brachah?"

"Brachah is Jewish and should be handed over to the Jewish Committee," answered Stashek.

"No," protested Marussa. "I won't give her to anyone here! She was given to me, and it's my responsibility to take care of her. It's dangerous for her to remain here."

"But where will you keep her outside of the ghetto?" Stashek asked. "Father won't permit her to enter our house. People ridicule us and treat us as if we were Jews. We must forget the past and not give anyone the opportunity to disparage us any more. And the law prohibits keeping Jews in any house outside the ghetto. If the Germans found out, we would be in danger."

"I'll put her in the convent, but I must save her life," Marussa answered. "Here she is in danger. If no one has come to take her back from me, that must mean that none of her relatives are alive, and I must take responsibility for her."

Stashek asked, "And what if they don't allow her to leave? Will you remain here because of her?"

Marussa reflected for a minute and then answered, "I will do what I can, but no more than that. If her own people, the Jews who guard the gate, don't allow her to leave, it will be their own fault. I will have done my share."

Stashek didn't continue the discussion. He silently prayed that the Jews at the ghetto gate would not let Brachah out and would save his family from this new trouble.

That very day, Stashek, holding Yanka in his arms, and

Marussa, holding Brachah's hand, all left the ghetto. The Jews at the ghetto gate did not detain them. Stashek's uniform and his and Marussa's Slavic faces served to obscure Brachah's Jewish eyes from the ghetto guards.

Stashek's prayers were not answered.

✧ 8 ✧ Escape

Yudel didn't go home. He couldn't bear to see the suffering of his in-laws. Furthermore, he didn't want to disclose Esther's secret to them. Perhaps they still held some slight hope of seeing her again, and he couldn't bring himself to extinguish this hope. Neither did he go to bring Brachah back from Marussa. Brachah would only ask about her mother, and he didn't know how to answer her questions. He therefore thought it better to wait a few days until Brachah was used to not seeing her mother. Chaim didn't ask about his mother. He wanted to, but when he looked into his father's face — suffused with suffering — he didn't ask.

Yudel went to Shimon's house. Shimon surpassed Yudel in both age and strength. Yudel had learned much Torah and that had worn away his physical strength. Shimon, on the other hand, was strong, and though he himself had learned little Torah, he held in high esteem those who had.

Shimon used to live on the ground floor of Reb Yisrael Reichman's house, outside of the ghetto. Whenever he would meet Yudel while passing by the gate, he would greet him loud and heartily. He didn't honor him for the sake of his father-in-law, the landlord, but for his own sake, because he was a *talmid chacham*.

In the ghetto, Shimon was no longer a tenant of Reb Yisrael Reichman who now had no house of his own. Actually, no one here had a house of his own. Even those whose present dwelling had once been their own no longer owned these homes. All the houses had been expropriated and belonged equally to all the homeless. Everyone had his own floor space in a room shared by a number of families.

Yudel went to Shimon's room. Shimon had also witnessed Esther's deed. He understood why Yudel couldn't go back to his father- and mother-in-law. He couldn't bear to see their suffering.

Shimon received Yudel warmly. He divided his floor space in two and bestowed one half on Yudel and Chaim. Shimon was a widower who had no children. He was also a carpenter — not an ordinary carpenter, but one with hands of gold and dexterous fingers which could build anything his eyes could see. In the ghetto, Shimon had received a grade A work-card, so his position was secure.

A week after Esther was taken away, Yudel went to fetch Brachah from Marussa, but no one was there. When he asked where Marussa had gone, the neighbors told him that she had left the house three days ago with a Polish student, holding Brachah's hand as they went. At first, Yudel was heartbroken.

"Apparently," he thought to himself, "Marussa left the ghetto and took Brachah with her after hearing of Esther's deed." But after thinking it over, he decided that perhaps Brachah was much safer outside the ghetto. When he, too, was able to leave the ghetto, he would go and take her from Marussa. Nevertheless, Yudel was unhappy. He tried to convince himself that it was all for the best, but he found no peace of mind — neither that day nor in the days that followed.

If he left the ghetto, he would get Brachah. But what would happen then? Would Brachah find her place among the Jewish people again? Yudel suffered greatly because of his daughter, in addition to the pain he suffered because of his wife. It would have been too much for any other man to bear, even for someone as strong as Shimon, but Yudel bore all that suffering within himself.

Yudel had many close friends in the ghetto, but Shimon was not one of them. Why then had he gone to Shimon rather than to one of the others? Yudel's heart told him that now was the time for him to stay close to Shimon, and his heart did not deceive him. Shimon was a simple person. He wasn't immersed in Torah, and neither was he an expert in other areas, but he was a proud Jew.

Whenever a Gentile would attempt to make fun of the Jews, Shimon would stand at the gate, ready to defend their honor. Once, when some Polish hooligans had thrown stones at the windows of the synagogue during the Prayer for Rain, Shimon had come out wearing his *tallith* and had smashed their bones, putting a few of them to bed until the time for the Prayer for Dew six months later. Shimon used to say, "It is good to hear the voice of Ya'akov in the synagogue, but not in the Gentile marketplace. In the synagogue one honors God with words, but in the marketplace one must honor Him with strength. When one fights the Gentiles, it is a *kiddush haShem.*" Shimon would have liked to fight in the ghetto, too, but he didn't know how to go about it. Nevertheless, he didn't give up.

One day, Shimon came home from work and found Yudel sitting and meditating. He asked, "What are you thinking about, Yudel?"

Yudel answered, "There is no lack of subjects for meditation in this ghetto."

"There is no value to such thinking," answered Shimon. "Something real must be done."

"What do you mean?" asked Yudel.

Shimon replied, "Come with me and we'll speak about action."

Yudel answered, "Talk has no substance either."

"You're right, Yudel," said Shimon. "Then let us not waste our words and not lose time. Let us act."

Yudel and Shimon left the room. Chaim remained at home with a few other people. When Yudel and Shimon arrived at their destination, others were already there. They were in a dark cellar whose only door was hidden from the outside by an old clothes cupboard. They pushed the cupboard to the side, opened the door, and entered the cellar. Then they returned the cupboard to its place, locked the door from the inside, and were well-hidden.

The discussion began. Shimon was one of its leaders. He began by saying, "After the incident with the girls, the time has come to do something." Everyone looked at Yudel and lowered their eyes.

"Are we all agreed?" asked Shimon.

Zechariah the butcher nodded his head.

"Well, Shimon, what has to be done?" asked Berel the porter.

Shimon looked Berel in the eyes and answered, "We have to get out of the ghetto." Then he added, "That is why we are here now—to figure out how to get out of the ghetto."

One of the group, whose face Yudel could not see because he sat further back in the darkness of the cellar, said, "Even if we find a way to get out, where can we go? All the Poles outside the ghetto are looking for Jews to hand over to the Gestapo."

"We can escape to Yanovsky forest, east of Nachrovah," said Shimon.

Another person shook his head and said, "Until we go, we won't know how to escape. Only after we've left will we know how we did it."

Shimon answered, "Nevertheless, we should know where to start."

Zechariah the butcher added, "Our Rabbis taught, 'If one rises up to kill you, kill him first.' We have to get rid of the guards at the ghetto gate, and then we can escape from the ghetto and flee to the forest. Not all of us together, like a herd, but each man for himself. Even if they pursue us, they won't catch everyone. Those who will get to the forest will get there, and those who don't make it will suffer no more. Endless suffering is worse than the end."

One of the group objected. "But Jews guard the gate. Shall we harm them?" This question was not answered.

Shimon turned to Yudel and asked, "And what does the Torah say about such a case?"

Yudel answered, "Every Jewish person is commanded to do all in his power to save his own life. We must escape from here and trust in God Almighty to send good angels to help us on our way."

Shimon asked, "Yudel, you said 'us.' Are you coming with us?"

Yudel answered, "Yes, I will go with you."

Shimon asked, "And will you take Chaim with you?"

"Yes," Yudel answered.

Shimon thought a bit and said, "We cannot leave here empty-handed. A man in the forest with no weapons is helpless. We must prepare weapons before we go." By the time they left the cellar it had already grown dark, and each man went his own way.

The next day, a Jewish *kapo* (policeman) approached Shimon at work and summoned him to Mr. Shefler, the head of the Jewish Committee. On his way to the committee office, Shimon stopped off at his home and found Yudel there. "I came to see if you were at home," said Shimon. "Perhaps you'll come with me to Mr. Shefler?" Yudel thought for a minute and then agreed.

When they entered the committee building, they saw many people and heard much crying. They entered Mr. Shefler's office, and he invited them to sit down. He looked into Shimon's eyes and said, "We hope that our troubles have come to an end. Jews will no longer be sent away. We have only to sit quietly and wait for the end of the war when we will be able to leave the ghetto. Meanwhile we must be careful not to endanger everyone in the ghetto by hasty actions."

Shimon heard but did not answer. He was shocked. How did Mr. Shefler learn of their plans? Was one of his group an informer? As Shimon made no reply, Mr. Shefler asked, "Why don't you answer me?"

"There was no question to answer," said Shimon.

Mr. Shefler saw that Shimon would not disclose his secret, and he stressed, "Anyone who dares to act without the approval of the Committee will be severely punished."

Then he turned to Yudel and said, "You are a *talmid chacham*. Tell me, does the Torah endorse endangering the community to save an individual?"

Yudel answered, "If it is for the good of one individual, it is certainly forbidden, but if it is for the good of many, then it is also for the good of the community. But I don't understand what you're talking about. I only came here with Shimon because I am his neighbor."

Mr. Shefler rose. "You may go now," he said. Then he turned to Shimon and added, "Remember, I warned you." Yudel and Shimon left the building.

It must be noted, in defense of Shimon's group, that none of them had turned informer. His own behavior those past few days had aroused suspicion. He was distracted and disorganized, always busy, but doing nothing. Anyone who looked into his eyes could read his thoughts. Shimon couldn't disguise the burning desire in his mind and his heart. He himself was the unwitting informer.

Mr. Shefler didn't depend on the warning he had given Shimon. He said to himself, "If Shimon does take action and tries to escape from the ghetto, Germans or Poles had better be standing guard at the gate, and not Jews. Otherwise they will blame me for cooperating with the runaways and my life will be worthless." For several days, only Poles guarded the ghetto gate, as Mr. Shefler had requested from the authorities. The reason he gave for this request is unknown to us. We followed behind Shimon and his men and paid no attention to Mr. Shefler.

One day, Shimon and his group took action. A few dozen young and not-so-young Jews, carrying weapons and accompanied by a few children, reached forest. Yudel and Chaim were among them, but Zechariah the butcher was not. His suffering reached its end before he reached the forest. In the struggle between the escapees and the guards, there were several casualties, and Zechariah was apparently among them. The escapees took some comfort in the fact that there were also casualties among the guards. Which side suffered greater casualties is not known. Those who escaped were too busy to stop and count the casualties at the gate.

⊸§ 9 §⊱ *Life in the Convent*

Happiness and sadness were both in Brachah's eyes. One minute her eyes smiled; the next moment they were on the verge of tears. She could not yet grasp the great change that had taken place. She was now in the company of five girls. Three of them were her own age, and two of them were about three years older. All of them wore clean clothes and whole shoes. She was also dressed in new clothes after the old clothes in which she had arrived were taken from her. Everything here was clean. In one room there were as many beds as there were girls. Six. Low chairs and tables were in a second room. Brachah was very comfortable sitting at such a table.

Marussa had brought her here this morning and had spoken to a middle-aged woman. The woman had listened to what Marussa was saying, all the while looking at Brachah. Brachah didn't understand what she was doing in this place, nor did she know who this woman was. When Marussa finished talking, the two women came over to Brachah. Marussa patted her head, said, "You will be very happy here, my child," and left. Then the other woman also caressed her and said, "From now on, you will stay with me. Call me Maria."

Brachah didn't know this Maria. She wasn't the same Maria who had worked in her grandfather's house. When Marussa had brought her here, Brachah thought that she was being taken to her parents, but now she saw that Marussa had not brought her to her father and mother, but to Maria. Maria wore a gray dress and a white apron. Her eyes were not dark like the eyes of most of the ghetto women. They were blue. Her hair, too, was not dark but light. She looked very much like Marussa. Perhaps they were sisters. Who knows…

Brachah stood and watched the girls, and the girls gazed back at Brachah. No one spoke. After a while, Maria broke the silence, turned to the girls, and said, "You have a new friend. Her name is Brachah. Come and talk to her. She too will be here with us." Then she left the room.

When Maria had left, the girls approached Brachah and asked, "Who brought you here?"

Brachah answered, "Marussa brought me."

The girls asked, "Who is Marussa? Is she your mother?"

"No," said Brachah. "My mother's name is Esther."

Sarah, the eldest of the girls, asked, "Where is your mother?"

Brachah answered, "In the ghetto."

Sarah said, "Don't be afraid, Brachah. We also come from the ghetto."

Brachah wanted to ask where she was, and who Maria was, but she didn't. She was too shy.

At 10 AM the girls went out to a yard which was enclosed by a tall, spiked fence painted green. You could see the street through the fence, but the spikes were dense so that from afar it was impossible to see into the yard. Well-dressed people walked up and down the street, and children played in the yards of the houses opposite. How different it all was from the ghetto! Brachah had never seen people dressed so well. Her heart rejoiced in what her eyes saw, until she remembered her mother and father and became sad. She also remembered Chaim and was jealous of him. Chaim was with Abba and Imma, so why was she here and not with them? There was no one to ask. The girls who were here with her surely did not know where her parents were.

Soon Maria called the four younger girls into the room. She sat them down at the low tables and handed each one a copybook and a pencil. The new copybook and pencil were for Brachah. The other three girls had been here for several weeks already, and Maria had begun teaching them to write a few days before.

Maria set up a small blackboard opposite them, and in white chalk she showed them how to write "father" and "mother" in Polish. She wrote beautiful, big, round letters on the board, and the girls tried to copy what Maria had written. The three other girls had some experience and had acquired some skill, but Brachah was trying her hand for the first time. She had never seen letters like these. In her parents' home she had seen books with completely different letters. Brachah knew how to speak Polish, because she had spoken to Maria who had worked in Grandfather's house. But she had never before seen letters like these.

Brachah tried to copy the two words. She wrote them anew on each of the twenty lines on the page. Each line looked better than the previous one. It was hard to read what she had written on the first lines, but the last ones were quite legible. For one hour the girls sat and wrote. When Maria announced that the lesson was over, they gave back the copybooks and pencils. Maria would return them at the next lesson.

While Brachah had been writing she had been absorbed in the work and hadn't thought about what she was writing. Now that she was finished, she began to think of the words, and tears came to her eyes. She had written "father" and "mother," but they were far away from here. Did they know where she was? Why hadn't they come to take her back from Marussa? Were they sick? Were Grandfather and Grandmother also sick? Was everybody sick? But when Brachah looked at the eyes of her friends and saw no tears, she dried her own tears and calmed down. The younger girls went out to the yard again, as the older girls came back in. Apparently they too were learning how to write.

At twelve o'clock the girls were called to dinner. They sat at the same tables at which they had written their lessons. A young woman whose dress was just like Maria's served them. Brachah looked at the food with amazement. She had not seen such food for a long time. White bread. Hot soup with meat. She was overwhelmed with happiness. Her mother had taught her to recite a *berachah* whenever she ate anything, so in a loud, joyous voice she said the appropriate *berachah* over each type of food. The girls looked at her, a bit startled. The young woman blushed. She looked at Brachah for a long time and finally left.

During the meal, the girls all talked with each other at

once. By now, Brachah knew all their names. Sarah was the oldest, and Rivkah came next. The three younger girls, Chavah, Leah and Rachel, were Brachah's age. They told Brachah that they had come from the ghetto a few weeks earlier. Sarah also knew why they had come. She said that there had been rumors in the ghetto that the Nazis were about to send away the children, and so their mothers had arranged to have them taken out of the ghetto, but she didn't know how. She did know that there were also boys in a similar house for boys.

Brachah asked Sarah, "If the Nazis were really going to take away the children, then why didn't they take me?"

Sarah answered, "Not everything they say in the ghetto is true. But perhaps it is true, and if they have not taken them away yet, they will do so tomorrow or the next day." Brachah was glad to be with the girls, where she would not be taken away.

After dinner the girls were told to lie down and rest for an hour. When they got up, they went to the yard. On her way out, Brachah noticed that the house contained several more rooms. In the corridor she met more women dressed just like Maria. She was a bit surprised that everyone wore the same clothing, but she liked the idea.

At night, before going to sleep, Maria told the girls that it was time to say their bedtime prayers. The five girls formed a line and then knelt on one knee, facing a corner of the room, the palms of their hands pressed together. Brachah looked at the corner and saw, above her friends' heads, a picture of a woman holding a little boy. Above the picture burned a small lamp which shed a dim light on it. Brachah wondered why she had not noticed the picture during the day. She looked at it again and saw that both the woman and the child in her arms were very sad. She said to herself, "His mother must be taking him out of the ghetto before the Nazis come to take him away."

Just then, Maria came up to Brachah and asked, "Why aren't you praying, Brachah?"

Brachah answered, "Before I go to sleep I recite *Shema Yisrael.*"

Maria said, "You must pray before the picture." Brachah couldn't understand the connection between the *Shema* her mother had taught her and this picture, but in order to satisfy Maria, she stood beside the girls facing the corner. Maria said, "Kneel on one knee." Brachah tried, but she couldn't do it. She had never stood on one knee and one foot. Maria helped Brachah to kneel, and then she too knelt down and began to pray. The girls repeated each verse after Maria.

Brachah didn't know the prayers that Maria was saying. She knew what her mother had taught her by heart, and that was easier for her. Brachah knelt on one knee, faced the picture, and whispered, "*Shema Yisrael,*" "Hear O Israel the Lord our God, the Lord is One." She didn't look at the picture because Imma had taught her to close her eyes while reciting the *Shema*, and you can't look at a picture with your eyes closed.

This incident was repeated the next morning. Brachah knelt on one knee before the picture and recited the *berachoth* that her mother had taught her to say every morning, her eyes closed. All the girls repeated what Maria said, but Brachah recited what she remembered of her mother's prayers.

Every day, Maria told the girls the name of the day. On Shabbath, she told them that it was Saturday. When Maria called the girls in for their writing lesson, Brachah was amazed. She knew that Shabbath was not like all other days. Certain things are not permitted on Shabbath, and writing is among those things. It is even forbidden to hold a pencil in one's hand. She wanted to ask Maria about this, but she was embarrassed. When Maria handed Brachah her copybook and pencil, Brachah took them weakly. Maria wrote on the blackboard in white chalk, "Tomorrow is a holiday," and the girls began to copy these words.

Brachah didn't know what to do. Imma had told her that it was forbidden to write on Shabbath, but Maria, who also knew what was forbidden and what was permitted, had told her to write. Brachah wrote "Tomorrow is a holiday" with shaking hands. That day, all the letters that Brachah wrote came out crooked. After the lesson, Maria collected Brachah's copybook but couldn't read it. The letters were so crooked they were illegible. Brachah had written much better yesterday. What had happened to her today?

At dinner, while Brachah was still preoccupied with the writing, another strange thing occurred to her. Why had Maria written, "Tomorrow is a holiday"? Was tomorrow really a holiday? Tomorrow was Sunday. Today, Shabbath, was a holiday, not tomorrow. This business with Maria was very puzzling. Brachah knew that Sarah and Rivkah were older than she and knew more than she did. In the yard, she therefore approached Rivkah and asked her about the writing. Rivkah looked at Brachah and laughed.

"What are you laughing at?" Brachah asked.

Rivkah answered, "Maria is a Christian, not a Jew. All of them here are Christian." Brachah looked into Rivkah's eyes but couldn't understand what Rivkah was saying. What were ghetto children doing with Christians?

Brachah's puzzle was not solved. On the contrary, it grew more confusing. When Rivkah saw that Brachah didn't understand her, she added, "You are still young. When you grow up a little, you'll understand everything." Brachah left Rivkah, full of sorrow that she would have to wait until she grew up before she could understand. Who knew how long that would take!

The second and third Shabbath, Brachah also wrote in a much poorer handwriting than she had during the rest of the week. Maria thought about this and discussed it with the other nuns. Brachah perplexed them. One of the nuns said, "Perhaps the Jews in the ghetto set some magic spell on her so that she would be unable to write on their Shabbath. The Jews always practice magic on the Christians."

The nuns were very much afraid when they heard their friend's opinion. If the Jews could control someone in the convent with their magic, who knew what other things they might do? But the nuns believed in Jesus and comforted themselves that he would protect them from Jewish magic.

Those who escaped from the ghetto of Nachrovah were the first to reach Yanovsky forest, but not the last. A few dozen Jews from the neighboring Temyonovah ghetto also escaped to the forest. The head of their group was Peretz the redhead. In peacetime he had been a tin worker and had prayed at the workers' synagogue, "Yad Charutzim." On Shabbath afternoons Peretz used to sit in the synagogue and listen to Reb Naftali the Dayan tell inspiring tales from the Midrash and Ein Ya'akov. When the stories were very sad, tears would well up in Peretz's eyes, as he shared the troubles of the Jewish people. When the stories were happy, he would stroke his red beard with visible enjoyment and rejoice with Israel.

Peretz was put into the ghetto with all the other Jews of Temyonovah, but not for long. On the very first day, he began plotting his escape. He dreamed of being one of those who arose to save the Jews in times of distress. He had always been jealous of these heroes when he heard about them from Reb Naftali the Dayan. He often thought to himself that if he had lived in the days of Bar Kochba, he would have joined his army. It was too bad there was no such person nowadays. On one hand, he held it against Bar Kochba for disappointing the great Rabbi Akiva by making Jewish boys cut off their thumbs to test their bravery, but he was also proud that such a person was Jewish. He admired his courage and bravery.

In the ghetto, Peretz felt that his hour had arrived. True, he was not as strong as Samson, nor was he a soldier like Bar Kochba, but every person is capable of doing something. What exactly he would do to save Israel he didn't yet know, but he did know that it would be easier to take action outside the ghetto than inside it. No prisoner can free others from jail. In order to free others, he would first have to free himself.

Peretz did in Temyonovah what Shimon had done in Nachrovah. He, too, with a few dozen other Jews, escaped from the ghetto, but his method of escape was different. He spent a few weeks digging a hole in the ground to make a tunnel from his room in the ghetto near the barbed-wire fence, to a deserted lot on the other side of the fence. Two other Jews helped him, but he did most of the work. The others got very tired after digging just a bit. Peretz was actually no stronger than they were, but sheer will power overcame any lack in his physical strength. When the tunnel was ready, Peretz revealed his secret to a few dozen members of his synagogue. One dark, cloudy night, when a storm had chased the Gentiles off the streets and pouring rain washed away all footprints, Peretz and his men left the ghetto for the street, and from there they continued to the forest.

After a short time, Shimon from Nachrovah and Peretz from Temyonovah became fast friends. They were happy to find each other, and they could help each other share the responsibility for the lives of the few dozen Jews, including several women and quite a few children. Peretz's own wife and twenty-year-old son had also come with him. Shimon and Peretz organized the camp in the forest. Since it was summer, the rainy season, and the women and children had to be protected from the rain, they cut branches from trees and built huts. The huts were not real houses; heavy rain could penetrate them, but at least they afforded protection against light rain. It felt good to have a roof of branches thick enough to hide the stars over their heads. The huts also afforded privacy. No man, and certainly no woman, wants to live in the street. A person needs four walls of his own.

Shimon and Peretz also accepted the responsibility for supplying the people in the forest with food. This was a job no one else could have done. They were familiar with the neighboring villages and would leave the forest every night, heading for a different village each time. They would knock on one of the village doors, and a farmer or his wife would open the door and stare open-mouthed. Opposite them stood two bearded "Jids," each one holding a rifle. The farmers wouldn't ask any questions — they would be too astonished to talk. Shimon would say his piece, and shortly after, Shimon and Peretz would leave, carrying with them sacks of food — bread, potatoes, and vegetables. Sometimes they paid more and sometimes less. When their money ran out, they didn't pay at all. Some of the farmers recognized Shimon and knew that this "Jid" could turn them into a pile of bones, even without a rifle, so they fulfilled his request for food quickly.

Shimon and Peretz knew that all these Poles were Jew-haters who could not be trusted not to betray them to the authorities. Therefore, they warned the Poles that anyone who told tales would meet a bitter end. Before the Germans could reach the Jews in the forest, the Jews would find out who had betrayed them and would punish that informer. The Poles knew that these were not mere threats, and they were careful. So far no one had said anything to the Germans; they didn't even talk about it among themselves. Each one kept his secret in order to protect his own life.

The partisans did not forget that their main purpose in escaping to the forest was not just to save their own skins, but to take revenge on the Nazis. Since they could not defeat them in face-to-face combat, they would do so by cunning and trickery. This was part of war. Among the weapons Shimon and Peretz had managed to smuggle out with them was a small amount of explosives — not a lot, but better than none at all. Now they had to make good use of it. The largest number of Nazis possible must be killed with this precious bit of explosives. Shimon and Peretz racked their brains until they hit upon an idea.

Nachrovah was the seat of the local Nazi headquarters. The headquarters building had formerly been the home of Reb Shloimeleh, the head of the Jewish community. When the Germans invaded Nachrovah, they seized the house. Reb Shloimeleh, displaced and dispossessed from his home, wandered from one place to another, until he and all the other Jews finally ended up in the ghetto. Now his house was marked as the partisans' target. It was the seat of all the plans hatched against the ghetto dwellers and must be blown up, together with the Nazi officers who occupied it daily. This building was the source of the death decree issued against thousands of guiltless Jews. The partisans knew that one act alone would not suffice to uproot all of the evil they were witnessing. Persons even more wicked might replace those who were killed, but every small victory over evil weakens its power to some extent, and revenge in such cases is very sweet.

Shimon called a meeting and announced the decision which had been reached. He asked for a volunteer to carry out the mission. It was clear that only someone from Nachrovah was eligible, someone who knew the town and all its pathways. Many Jews from Nachrovah volunteered, including Yudel Glick. Shimon chose Yudel. He could be counted on not to let them down. If necessary, he would even sacrifice his life.

The date was set for the following evening. At night, the Nazis left their headquarters one by one until only a few officers remained on duty. Therefore the act would have to be carried out at the beginning of the night.

At that time the British were bombing the German airfields, one of which was close to Nachrovah. To prevent the enemy from locating the airfield, it was necessary to enforce a blackout for several kilometers around it. Thanks to this blackout, Yudel would be able to approach Reb Shloimeleh's house unnoticed and to leave a small pitcher of explosives against the back wall. Yudel didn't understand the mechanism inside the pitcher — Shimon and Peretz had built the bomb. All Yudel knew was that he had to lean the pitcher against the northern wall of the house at 9:00 PM;

half an hour later, the explosives would work automatically. During that half hour he had to get back to the forest, at the entrance of which he would hear the explosion.

That night, Yudel couldn't fall asleep — but not because he was afraid of his mission the following evening. After all, no one had asked him to volunteer. No, it was the natural reaction of one who was about to carry out an important mission and couldn't take his mind off the act. While Yudel, his eyes closed, was picturing himself carrying out his task, he suddenly saw a circle of young girls. He narrowed his eyes to watch the circle and saw that they were dancing a dance the likes of which he had never seen before. They all moved simultaneously, as if they were one person, not many. He looked at their faces and saw that they all looked alike. This seemed a wondrous thing to him. Twins could be identical, but not strangers. The girls were singing, "Nevertheless we have not forgotten Thy Name." They repeated this verse over and over. Yudel racked his brain trying to remember the words preceding this verse. Finally he remembered: "We were as sheep brought to slaughter — to kill and wipe out, for blows and for shame." The last words echoed in his mind. For shame. For shame. For shame.

After he had thought of the verse he looked at the girls' faces again, and his heart stopped. The face of one of the girls now looked like that of Esther. His Esther. He saw that Esther was much taller than the other girls. She led them in the circle, and they all followed her.

When Esther passed by, she suddenly turned towards him, looked at him, and stopped walking. They stood opposite each other. She looked at him and he at her. After a silence, Esther smiled and asked him, "Where is Brachah?" Yudel didn't know what to answer. Esther's face saddened, and she said, "Brachah must be saved." Yudel knew it was his fault—he had not gone to get Brachah back from Marussa—and he lowered his eyes.

When he looked again, he no longer saw Esther. He saw Brachah sitting on the dome of a church, her tiny hand holding on to the cross in order not to fall off. Yudel stretched out his arms so that he could catch her when she let go of the cross. At that minute he felt someone hit his arm and he woke up. He was terribly upset by his dream. For a long time he couldn't compose himself.

Finally, he made a decision. He would find Brachah, come what may. She was in Nachrovah with Marussa, not far from where he was. He must find a way to locate Marussa. He knew where her father's house was. He must go there. Of course, he realized that this was dangerous. If he were seen in a Polish house, the Poles would inform on him to the Nazis. But he must not abandon Brachah. Perhaps, after his action the next day, the Poles in Nachrovah would realize that the Jews of the forest knew how to take revenge, and it would be less of a risk to be seen in a Polish house. In the future, perhaps they would not dare to inform on the Jews.

When dawn broke, Yudel got up. He washed his hands and recited the *berachoth* over the Torah. Then he put on his *tallith* and *tefillin* and prayed with great devotion. He tried to take his mind off his dream, but he was unsuccessful. It had set his soul afire. All that day Yudel was distracted and could find no peace of mind.

An hour before dark, he took the pitcher with the explosives and started out for the city. He had to be at the edge of the forest exactly at nightfall in order to reach the headquarters at the appointed time. Shimon accompanied Yudel part of the way and showed him exactly what to do. When they parted, Shimon wished Yudel success. Yudel thanked him weakly. He had not yet recovered from his dream of the night before.

In order not to arouse suspicion, Yudel wore farmer's clothes. His pitcher was covered with a lid and might have contained milk or fruit. His beard was concealed by a scarf, as he would not allow it to be cut off. After sunset, he left the forest and followed a dirt trail. By the time he reached the town, it was pitch black. It was the end of the month, and there was no moon and no stars, only a cloudy sky.

Yudel arrived at the headquarters exactly at nine o'clock. He walked behind the house on the northern side. There was no entrance there, and no one ever passed that way. He put the pitcher down quickly, leaning it against the wall, and immediately left the site. Now he had only to return to the forest, east of the town.

As Yudel passed Catholichka Street, he heard a familiar voice call, "Abba!" Yudel trembled. He stood still and looked around to see where it was coming from. To his left he saw the convent, a cross rising from its dome. Could Brachah possibly be in that building? No, it must be his imagination. All day he had been so preoccupied with his dream that now he imagined he heard Brachah's voice. But whether the voice was real or imagined, his heart was filled with boundless suffering.

As Yudel stood there, a man came up to him and asked whom he was looking for. Yudel mumbled some kind of an answer which did not satisfy the questioner. He grabbed Yudel's arm and said, "Come with me." As they were walking, the Pole examined Yudel carefully. "You are not one of us," he said.

Yudel didn't answer. He was so absorbed in his own thoughts that he didn't even hear what the Pole had said. As they came closer to headquarters, Yudel suddenly remembered that the building was about to be blown up. He tried to resist and to run away from the Pole. He was not afraid for his own life, but he had to take care of Brachah and Chaim. But the Pole was stronger than Yudel and forced him into the building. A German officer asked him his name and occupation, but before Yudel had a chance to answer, the entire house was lifted up into the air and then fell back down. In its place, there was now a pile of stones, with all the contents of the house buried underneath.

Echoes of the explosion reached the forest. The partisans rejoiced at Yudel's success. Now they knew that he had carried out his mission faithfully. They waited impatiently for his return so that he could tell them all about his feat. But hour after hour passed and Yudel didn't come. They began to worry.

The next day, several Poles reported that they had left the building shortly before the explosion occurred, and as they were leaving they had seen a Jew forcibly brought into the building. When the partisans heard this from one of the village farmers, they knew that Yudel would never return to the forest.

Peretz was envious. He said, "Yudel died just like the mighty Samson. Samson prayed, 'Let me die with the Philistines,' and Yudel prayed, 'Let me die with the Nazis.' What a beautiful death. What a beautiful death," Peretz repeated over and over.

When Brachah cried out "Abba," Sarah jumped out of bed
and went over to her. She took Brachah's hand in her own
and said, "You must have been dreaming, Brachah."

"No," Brachah answered, "I wasn't dreaming."

"Then why did you cry 'Abba'?"

"I saw my father passing by the house," Brachah
answered.

"How could you see your father passing by the house
while you were lying in bed? Even if you were standing by
the window, you couldn't have seen him pass by. It's dark
outside."

"I don't know how I saw him, but I saw him."

"You were dreaming, Brachah, and you thought it
really happened."

Brachah didn't answer. She closed her eyes and fell
asleep, and Sarah went back to bed.

At prayers the next morning Brachah refused to bow
down before the icon in the corner of the room, even when
Maria ordered her to do so. Maria couldn't understand what
had happened. Every day Brachah behaved just like all the
other girls — why was today different? Maria asked Brachah,

but Brachah didn't answer. Instead, she looked at Sarah and kept her silence. Maria understood that there was some secret between Sarah and Brachah. She decided to investigate — not now in front of all the girls, but later. After breakfast when the girls had gone out to play in the yard, Maria summoned Sarah to her room and began to question her about Brachah. Sarah told Maria about Brachah's dream while Maria listened, bewildered. Earlier that morning she had heard about the Jew who had been carried off to the Gestapo headquarters just a few minutes before it was blown up. Everyone realized that this was the man who was responsible for the deed. He had died a hero's death. Even though he knew what was about to happen he had not attempted to save his own life by telling the Germans. According to Sarah, Brachah had cried "Abba" shortly after the girls had gone to bed. Bedtime was before 9:00 PM. Had that Jew really passed by the convent? If so, was he Brachah's father? Even if he were Brachah's father, how could she have seen him while she was lying in bed?

Maria's head was filled with questions to which she could find no answers. It was all very mystifying. She told the story to the other nuns, and one of them said, "The Jews have practiced their witchcraft on Brachah. Her soul must be saved. She must be treated very severely. Her stubborn refusal to bow down and pray is not her own; it represents the will of all the Jews in the ghetto. Even now in the ghetto, the Jews continue to deny Jesus, and they suffer for their heresy. There is no hope for them. God has cursed them. But some few can be saved. Brachah can be saved. However, we must treat her very severely." She repeated her opinion over and over until Maria was convinced of its truth.

From that day on, Maria stopped smiling at Brachah. Her tone of voice turned Brachah's bones to ice. During writing class, Maria continuously found fault with Brachah's work and rebuked her for not doing as well as her classmates. The five girls who had been Brachah's friends saw that Maria was angry at Brachah, and they too withdrew from her. They feared that Maria would be angry with them if they remained friends with Brachah. Maria did everything for them. They needed her and wished to stay in her favor.

Brachah wept alone. She felt that her heart would break. She had no one to talk to. The children laughed and played with one another, but shunned her. Brachah withdrew into herself. She pressed her lips together, determined to remain silent. She did not answer Maria's questions. She did not bow before the icon. At prayer time, she recited the *Shema*, morning and evening, her eyes closed and her head upright. Her father's image never left her. She knew that he would not want her to bow down before the picture of the mother and child. He had never told her so explicitly, but he himself had never done so, and she would not either. When her father's image was before her eyes, he was always smiling, not like Maria and all her friends. Whenever Brachah's heart grew cold and lonely, she would close her eyes and see her father smiling at her, and she would feel warm and happy.

Brachah grew pale; from day to day she seemed to shrivel. She ate almost nothing and withdrew deep into herself. Who knows what might have happened to Brachah had Marussa not come. Marussa saved her body, but not her soul.

Since Marussa had left the ghetto and returned home to her parents, she hardly ventured outside. She couldn't bear the scorn that she had brought upon herself. Is there any greater shame for a Christian woman than to marry a Jew? Even now, when Mr. Shmendrikovitz had disappeared, Marussa's shame had not lessened. Marussa was aware of what people were saying about her, and she avoided them. She even began to doubt herself and to wonder if it really had been wise for her to marry Yank. Even so, she was furious at her countrymen for siding with the Germans — Poland's eternal enemies.

And she could not understand why the convents should welcome Jewish children from the ghetto if they mocked her for marrying a man who had converted to Christianity. Weren't the Poles contradicting themselves? Marussa sat at home and spun her thoughts into a thread which grew longer and longer.

Then suddenly, Marussa's status changed overnight. When the Poles heard of the explosion at the Gestapo headquarters they could not help but be impressed and full of admiration for the heroic act. With one blow, a Jew had wiped out dozens of German officers and workers and had paralyzed the work of the headquarters for a long time to come. All the documents which the Germans had worked so hard and so long to amass were lost, and the confusion and loss of information which this caused would cost the Germans many precious months of work.

The Poles began to respect the Jews. They did not often praise them, but their silence reflected their envy. Soon after, Marussa began to venture outside her house. When her former friends met her now, they lowered their eyes. She had gained their respect, and they no longer mocked her. Although she was a Christian, just as they were, they looked upon her as a Jewish heroine. It was as though she herself had carried out the heroic act in the headquarters, or as though the Jew who did so were her brother.

It was then that Marussa came to the convent to visit Brachah. She had been in a good mood and had thought of her. When Marussa heard of Brachah's dream, her heart skipped a beat. And when she heard of Brachah's sad plight since that day, her heart fell within her. She asked to see Brachah, and Maria went to the courtyard to summon the girl. As she was about to enter the room, Brachah caught sight of Marussa. For a moment, she was confused and stood rooted to the spot. Then she let out a great cry and ran to Marussa. Marussa caressed the excited girl and hugged her with all her might. She sat Brachah on her lap and stroked her head until she calmed down and stopped crying.

Marussa signaled Maria to leave the room, and when they were alone, she asked Brachah many questions but received few answers. Finally Marussa said that Maria was a good woman who wished to help Brachah, and that Brachah should obey and try to love her. She, Marussa, would come now and then to visit; meanwhile Brachah should behave like all the other girls. They had all come from the ghetto and were no different from her. Marussa might have continued talking to Brachah for a long time had not Maria interrupted them to announce that it was time for the writing lesson. Marussa rose, kissed Brachah goodbye, and promised to come again soon.

From that day on, Brachah obeyed Maria and behaved just like the other girls. She even knelt on her knee before the picture of the mother and child.

◄§ 12 ৯► *Chaim*

Although no one discussed what had happened to Yudel in front of Chaim, Chaim understood. He read in their eyes what they would not say aloud. At first, he wanted to ask why his father hadn't come back to the forest, but in the end, he didn't. He was afraid to hear the answer which he already knew. Shimon befriended Chaim and took him under his wing, and Chaim gave his silent assent. In their free time, Shimon would sit with Chaim and talk to him so that he would not be so lonely.

Once, Chaim asked Shimon about his sister, Brachah. Since the day they had left their house in the ghetto for that fateful line-up behind the burnt synagogue, he had not seen Brachah. He had no idea where she was. As long as his father was with him, he had not asked about her because he was sure his father knew where Brachah was and was taking care of her. But now that his father was no longer with him, Brachah began to dominate his thoughts, so he asked Shimon about her.

Chaim assumed that Brachah had remained in the ghetto, and when the war was over, they would be reunited. He was amazed to hear that Brachah had left the ghetto with a Christian woman and was now in Nachrovah. He couldn't understand how Brachah could be in the town when he and the other Jews in the forest were not allowed there.

At first he was jealous, but later, he began to worry about her. Wasn't it dangerous for a Jewish girl to remain in Nachrovah outside the ghetto? He began to see Brachah in his dreams. Each time he saw her he rejoiced, although he knew that these were merely dreams. He began to realize that now, since his father and mother were gone, no one but he would worry about her. He didn't yet know how he could help her, but he did know that he must not forget her, and so he rejoiced to see her. These dreams would prevent him from forgetting her.

Chaim had several different dreams about Brachah. Sometimes he would picture her sitting at a table and eating a rich meal — white bread with butter and other foods whose names he had forgotten. He hadn't eaten such foods for a long time, and he was happy to see his sister eating them.

Another time he saw her standing at the window of a nice house, her eyes searching for someone. Her face was sad and her eyes red from crying. He shouted to her with all his strength to let her know that he saw her, but she neither saw nor heard him.

Chaim did not always remember his dreams the next day, but he always remembered that he had seen Brachah, and this was sufficient cause for him to rejoice. Chaim also told himself that if he remembered her, she must remember him, and so he was not alone in the world. Someone was thinking of him. Of course, Shimon thought of him and took care of him, but Shimon was not his relative. It was good to have a sister who thought of him.

Chaim would lie for hours, his eyes closed, trying to picture Brachah. At first he would not succeed. Only after his intense efforts had worn him out, and his skinny body was covered with sweat, would Brachah appear to him in a dream. People wondered at his strange habits, as most children do not usually lie idle for hours at a time.

When he was on his feet, Chaim was quick and daring. Shimon had taught him to be brave. He assigned him to guard duty far away from the camp towards the city. Chaim stood at his post fearlessly, listening for suspicious sounds. This guard duty was an innovation, begun after Yudel's exploit, as the partisans were afraid that the Germans would attempt to attack them. Shimon did not assign Chaim to guard duty from any lack of able-bodied men, but in order to train him not to be a coward. Guard duty gave Chaim pride and self-confidence. It also strengthened his feeling that, as a strong, mature person, he would be able to help his sister.

Peretz also befriended the orphaned Chaim for the sake of his father. To Peretz, Yudel was like one of the great heroes he had heard of in Reb Naftali the Dayan's stories. Shimon took charge of Chaim's physical needs, and Peretz took charge of his education. Although Peretz had little formal education and there were no Torah books in the forest, he taught Chaim all that he remembered of the wonderful tales of Reb Naftali the Dayan. He told him of Rabbi Akiva ben Yosef and his followers and of Bar Kochba and his army. He told him tales of Eretz Yisrael and of Yerushalayim, the Holy City; of the *Beith haMikdash*, the

Holy Temple that was twice destroyed; and of the *Kothel haMa'aravi*, the Western Wall, which remains standing to this day.

Chaim absorbed all of Peretz's stories. His favorites were the stories about the Ba'al Shem Tov. Peretz described the palaces which the Ba'al Shem Tov and his followers found in the forest one Friday just before sundown, when snow buried the whole world and the horses were unable to draw the carriages and their passengers to their destination before Shabbath. While listening to this story, Chaim would imagine that he and all the Jews of Yanovsky forest were the holy Ba'al Shem Tov's disciples. His eyes closed, he would see himself in the palace. Chaim was especially fond of Peretz because of these tales, which both comforted and inspired him. Peretz also enjoyed his role as storyteller. Although the stories were not new to him, they took on new life as he told them. He had always listened to others speak and had never realized that he himself was gifted. Now, as he became aware of his talents as a storyteller, each tale, as he told it, appeared in a new light to him.

One day Shimon posted Chaim on guard duty about two kilometers from the camp. He was told to listen for suspicious sounds from the direction of Nachrovah. Chaim had done this many times before. When on duty, he never allowed himself to sink into reveries about Brachah or muse over Peretz's tales, but he would concentrate on listening.

Why that day was different was a mystery to Chaim. He had always been able to stand for hours, but today it was hard for him. He sat down and leaned against a tree trunk. It was a quiet noon. The thick forest protected Chaim from the sun's rays. Chaim, like all the children in Yanovsky forest, was weak. He saw white bread and butter only in his dreams, and even then it was Brachah, not he, who was enjoying them. What he ate — black bread and potatoes cooked in their skins — was not enough to sustain his small body. All he drank was water, which was sometimes not fit for drinking. Apparently he was too weak today to stand up. Today, he didn't even have the strength to sit for long, so he stretched out on the ground. Lying down, one could press his ear to the earth and hear even better than sitting or standing. The earth is the ally of the oppressed. It exposes the footsteps of those who pursue them.

Chaim lay on the ground contentedly. He had not slept on a pillow for a long time. To him there was nothing sweeter than to lie on the ground. He recalled how Ya'akov Avinu, may he rest in peace, had slept on a pillow of stones when fleeing from Esau. If Ya'akov could sleep on stones without complaining, then Chaim would surely not complain, because the ground is much softer than stones.

After a while, Brachah appeared before his eyes. She was standing in the yard of a nice building and looking about her. Chaim came close to her, wanting to surprise her, but when he got very close he was stopped by a wall. Chaim walked the length of the wall, searching for the opening, but he couldn't find it. He was amazed. In front of him was a high wall; nevertheless he could see Brachah. But how could mortal eyes penetrate a wall? Chaim tried to catch Brachah's eye. If he succeeded, she would show him how to reach her.

For a long time he stared at her unceasingly so that she would turn around and look at him. Once he had heard from adults that staring at someone causes him to look back in response. He was sure that she would see him, and he was right. Brachah turned around and looked straight into his eyes. At that moment, Chaim was about to ask Brachah how he could reach her, but her look frightened him. She gave him such a cold stare that he froze.

How could Brachah not recognize him? Even if she didn't recognize his face, she must recognize her own. Weren't they as identical as two drops of water? She must know who he was, but in her anger, she was refusing to smile at him. He had no idea why she should be so angry. After all the time that he had devoted to her, she had spurned him. Chaim gestured to Brachah to come towards him but she didn't move. She stood where she was as if she didn't see him. Chaim's heart was broken. Brachah had rejected him. He had tried to rescue her and she had rejected him! What a fool! How ungrateful! He wasn't really angry at her, for she seemed so very young. Perhaps she didn't understand. Nonetheless, he was extremely hurt.

Suddenly, Chaim heard a loud noise. He turned his head in all directions to identify its source. It seemed to be coming from all sides at once. Chaim turned his attention back to Brachah, but she had disappeared. To his astonishment, the house and the yard had also disappeared. His attention was drawn back to the noise, which grew increasingly louder. He began to be afraid. Now he was happy that Brachah was no longer there to hear the noise. She would have been frightened. Chaim suddenly remembered that Shimon had stationed him there to notify him of any suspicious sounds. He wanted to run back to the camp, but someone was holding his hand. He tried to withdraw it but was too weak.

When Chaim finally opened his eyes, he saw many people around him. Frightened, he jumped up. The people looked at him with curiosity and asked him his name and the location of the Jews' camp in the forest. Chaim didn't answer their questions, but they understood why and didn't interrogate him any further. They tried to reassure him by saying that they were Poles, not Germans. Chaim himself had realized this, as he knew Polish and understood their conversation, but this was small comfort to him, for he knew that the Poles also hated the Jews. Chaim felt terrible. What would he tell Shimon? He had not carried out his orders. He had failed to do his duty and was ashamed of himself.

The men took Chaim with them and continued on their journey eastward into the forest.

Yudel's bravery had lowered the self-esteem of Stashek and his friends. Cowardly Jews had performed a heroic deed, while they, the Polish patriots, had not yet accomplished anything worthwhile. All they had done so far was talk endlessly about the need to take action against the Germans. They also envied the Jews their new popularity and respect. They hated the Jews and couldn't bear to hear other Christians praise them. At last, when they could find no other alternative, they decided to follow in the Jews' footsteps and take to the forest to fight the Germans from there.

During that period, Stashek was much more at ease among his friends. In their efforts to salvage their own honor, they stopped deriding the Jews. Now that Stashek no longer had to bear the jeering looks of his friends, he could relax.

They set the date for their venture to the forest for a week from Sunday. Why Sunday? On Sunday, the Christian day of rest, people would take long walks, in and out of town. The group planned to simply walk out of town towards the forest. Once they entered the forest, they would be at war with the Germans. It was much easier to reach the forest in the daytime, during a leisurely walk, than to flee there at night.

That week, they stocked up on everything that a partisan might need. They prepared pistols, explosives, and food for a day or two. They also had a few rifles, but you can't carry a rifle when you're out for a walk. Antek would bring the rifles at night, in a wagon covered with straw. He would drive up to the edge of the forest, and they would pick them up there.

They were in high spirits all week. Now they would not need to be embarrassed by the heroic deed of that cursed Jew. They would show everyone in Nachrovah that the Poles are braver than the Jews. The Jew's accomplishment was an exception to the rule, but they would perform many such deeds. It may be said in their praise that all week they waited impatiently for Sunday to come. They became more and more envious of the Jews and impatient to redeem themselves from the disgrace of inaction.

On Sunday morning they went to church. They listened to the priest's sermon, enjoining them to cooperate with the authorities. His words disturbed them a bit but were quickly forgotten. They prayed hastily. Their knees touched the church floor, but their hearts were already in the forest.

After leaving the church, they all gathered at a friend's house and drank a substantial toast to their success. Their jubilance swelled, both because of the strong drink and because of their imminent departure to Yanovsky forest.

As they drank they discussed their venture. One of the group wondered if they should ally themselves with the Jews in the forest or keep their distance from them. A friend answered that they must keep away from the Jews. If they were to cooperate, no one would know afterwards who had carried out the heroic acts they planned to perform.

In the afternoon they split into several innocent looking groups. Each group walked around town, then out of town, and finally into Yanovsky forest. They remained at the edge of the forest, however, not penetrating deep inside, for they didn't want to meet with the Jews. Towards evening Antek brought the things they had not carried with them on their walk, and the Polish partisans set up camp.

Now the Poles in the forest did just what the Jews had done several months before. They put up huts. It was much easier for the Poles than it had been for the Jews. The Jewish camp included women and children, while the Polish camp was comprised of men only. There was another difference. The men in the Jewish camp were not all young — even Shimon and Peretz were not so young anymore — while in the Polish camp they were all young.

Several days passed and the Poles began to plan their action against the Germans. So far they had not accomplished anything. Whatever action they had taken was in the villages. The food they brought with them was gone in two days' time, and they began to steal into the villages at night for supplies. In this they were more successful than the Jews. They were blood brothers to the Polish farmers and were highly regarded by them, so that unlike the Jews, they did not have to resort to threats in order to obtain a little food.

But the Poles' complacency was short-lived. The Germans dispatched new officers to Nachrovah to replace those killed by Yudel. They found another house in place of the one that had been destroyed, and they once again began to take action against Jews and against Poles who collaborated with Jews.

The Germans had heard rumors about partisans in the forest, and they feared that actions such as the explosion at the German headquarters would be repeated. As their fear grew, they decided to surround the forest and capture all those hiding within. If they succeeded, there would no longer be any threat of danger, and they would be able to continue exterminating the Jews undisturbed.

One morning the Poles heard suspicious sounds coming from the edge of the forest. Listening carefully, they realized that these were German voices, not Polish ones. They looked at one another and estimated the risk. Quickly, they took down their huts, packed their belongings, and began to move deeper into the forest.

Truth to tell, they panicked unnecessarily. The danger was not imminent, for the Germans were afraid to enter the forest. They wanted the partisans to come out to them. Outside the forest, they had the advantage. They possessed tanks and planes, whereas the Jews and Poles only had rifles and pistols. Inside the forest, the Germans lost their advantage. They therefore tried to scare the partisans out of the forest by raising a great ruckus nearby. Had the Poles not run away, the Germans would probably not have attacked them. But the Poles, not realizing that the Germans too were cowards, fled deeper and deeper into the forest.

As they cut further into the forest, they found Chaim asleep on the ground, his hands and legs stretched out and his face turned towards the town. They recognized him as a

Jewish child, one of the group of partisans. This meant that they must be close to the Jewish camp. Stashek looked at Chaim and wondered silently, "That face is familiar. Where have I seen it before?" He couldn't remember. "Perhaps with my sister Marussa? No, Marussa had a girl with her, not a boy." Stashek took hold of Chaim's hand and gazed at him for a long time, trying to remember where he had seen him before, until finally he gave up. When Chaim woke up he took his hand away from Stashek, frightened and upset.

The Poles made no attempt to talk to Chaim as they walked. They knew he would not answer their questions, because he didn't trust them. That's the way the Jews always were. They lived on Polish soil but distrusted their Polish overlords. It was not for nothing that the Jews were disliked. On the way, Stashek kept glancing at Chaim, trying unsuccessfully to remember where he had seen him. Still racking his brain, he arrived with the others at the Jewish camp.

In the camp, no one heard them coming. The Poles had walked in silence, each one contemplating the imminent confrontation with the Jews. When the Jews first saw their guests, they recognized them and did not panic. They realized that these were not German agents. Shimon, the commander of the camp, took a few steps towards them. He was the first to greet them. The Poles returned his greeting, smiling like old friends who were meeting after a long separation.

Shimon waited for the Poles to speak first. They were the guests so it was up to them to state the purpose of their visit. The Poles, about thirty of them, spread out in a wide formation. Yashek, who was their commander, stepped forward and offered his hand to Shimon. Shimon took Ya-shek's hand and shook it heartily. Yashek stated that they had come to the forest to fight the Germans. Since the Jews were also at war with the Germans, the Germans were their common enemy, and it would be advantageous to combine their strength to fight them. Shimon nodded his head in agreement and with a generous gesture invited the guests to enter the camp.

Shimon's eyes searched the group of Poles, looking for Chaim. Where was he? How was it that he had not seen them coming? How had the Poles not seen Chaim? All this time Chaim had stood behind the line of Poles. He was greatly afraid and even more embarrassed. When Shimon finally saw Chaim hiding behind the Poles, he heaved a sigh of relief. He called Chaim to him and smiled at him benevolently. Chaim was very pale and his whole body quaked, but when he saw Shimon's smile, he felt better. Relieved, he began to weep for joy.

◦⊰ 14 ⊱◦ *Cain and Abel*

Gradually, the two camps developed friendly relations. Suspicions faded and were replaced by mutual trust. People tend to believe what is most convenient for them, and at that time it was most convenient for both the Poles and the Jews to live together as friends, not as enemies.

It was the end of summer. Winter was just around the corner for Nachrovah, Temyonovah, and for Yanovsky forest between them. In the winter the temperature would fall far below zero and everything would freeze over. Anyone wanting to survive would have to provide himself with some means of defense against the cold. In Nachrovah and Temyonovah, people fought the cold by sealing themselves in rooms heated by wood furnaces; in the forest they would flee underground.

In the partisans' camp they dug caves. Even though they lived in one camp, there would be separate caves for Jews and for Poles. There was no formal decision about this, but it was taken for granted. People are most comfortable among their own kind. Poles like to talk about certain topics in one language while Jews talk about other topics in another language. Peretz's stories, for instance, would not be appreciated by the Poles. Since the Jews and Poles were not going to live together, each group dug its own cave.

The fact that they were not digging together did not disturb the friendship between the two groups of partisans. It was taken for granted and did not arouse anger or hatred. The Poles' cave was ready first. Thirty pairs of young Polish hands could work much faster than those of the Jewish partisans. In the Jewish group, the women and children did not participate in the digging, and many of the men were not so young. When the Poles had finished their own cave, they helped the Jews. Everyone was in high spirits, and mutual help was the order of the day.

The winter would bring both cold to the world and warmth to the caves. The snow covering the ground above the caves would protect and insulate them against the cold. The digging took several days, during which time they did nothing else. When they were finished, they remembered that they hadn't come to Yanovsky forest to dig caves, but to fight the Germans, and they began to think.

The Poles were especially anxious to act quickly as they had already been in the forest for a few weeks and had not yet accomplished anything. They knew that their townspeople were waiting to hear of their exploits. The Poles are a proud people whose reputation is very dear to them. They were eager for their countrymen to hear of their bravery. The Jews were also eager to take action against the Germans. They had no need to justify their escape to the forest, but they knew that in weakening and defeating the Germans they would be saving their own lives.

The group commanders sat and debated what course of

action to take. After hearing various proposals, they decided in favor of what seemed to be the best one: Not far from the forest ran the railroad tracks which were used by various trains, including those which transported German soldiers eastward to the Russian front. They would find out exactly when the transport would pass by and blow it up.

This idea was not original; such exploits had already been reported in the papers. Although the newspapers were censored and incidents such as these were played down by the Germans, people read between the lines and were quite impressed. This would be an easy mission for the partisans of Yanovsky forest as the railroad ran the length of the forest less than two kilometers away. It would be simple to blow up a train passing by in the middle of the night. Two partisans had only to reach the tracks under cover of darkness, place explosives on the tracks, and return to the forest before the explosion.

Vachek and Paltiel were chosen to carry out the deed. Vachek had studied engineering and would set the time for the explosion. Paltiel would help him and would also carry the explosives to the tracks. Yashek ascertained the train schedule from one of the station workers. The train would pass through the forest at two o'clock in the morning, a convenient hour for terrorist action. At one-thirty Paltiel would bring the explosives to the train tracks. Vachek would supervise their placement, attach a string about five meters long, and a minute before the train was about to pass, he would light the string and retreat quickly. There would be just enough time for him to run a few meters away and hide behind a small hill nearby. Then, during the commotion following the explosion, the partisans would be able to retreat back into the safety of the forest.

Why had Shimon seen fit to choose Paltiel? He was strong, a porter by trade, and could carry the explosives easily. Shimon also thought that it was wise for any Jew accompanying a Pole at night to be stronger than the Pole. This would prevent the Pole from being tempted to harm the Jew, and it would enable the Jew to protect himself. Paltiel, a simple, good-hearted Jew who trusted everyone, did not follow Shimon's line of thought. He was simply proud to have been chosen for the task and happy to do something to help others.

The next day Vachek and Paltiel prepared themselves for action. Vachek prepared the explosives, weighed them, and measured the string, while Paltiel stood and watched. His part was less complicated. He was only Vachek's porter and aide. At one o'clock in the morning Vachek and Paltiel left the camp, a package on Paltiel's shoulder and a rifle in Vachek's hand. At one-twenty-five they reached the edge of the forest. There they stopped for a few seconds and listened in all directions. All was still.

They walked towards the tracks, without a word. Silence is appropriate at such a time. At one-thirty they arrived at the railroad tracks. Vachek tapped Paltiel on the shoulder, and he set down his package. They both stood and listened attentively. The silence was undisturbed. Vachek put his mouth to Paltiel's ear and whispered to him to pull the package another few steps. Then he took the package from Paltiel and motioned to him to wait behind a small hill.

Paltiel walked to the place Vachek had indicated and sat

down on the ground behind the hill. Vachek remained near the tracks. Paltiel had to wait only half an hour for Vachek, but it seemed to him a million years. When would the train come? Paltiel strained his ears and imagined that he heard the train coming. His heart began to pound. But minutes passed and the train didn't come. Paltiel was greatly disappointed. The same thing happened a second time. The third time that Paltiel heard the train coming he didn't believe it. But when he saw a bright light from the west, he knew that this time it really was the train. His heart stopped. Every second was endless. He lay flat on the ground. Just then he felt a hand tap him, and he knew that Vachek had arrived and that in less than a minute there would be an explosion.

Paltiel was completely gripped by the excitement of the impending explosion. Suddenly his ears were deafened by a powerful blast that shook the world. And just when a great light from the explosion lit up the entire area, Vachek pressed the trigger of his gun and shot Paltiel in the heart.

If Paltiel managed to let out even one groan, it was swallowed up by the noise of the explosion. After that Vachek took off his cap and shot two holes in its visor. He replaced his cap and started on his way back through the forest.

The partisans in the forest had heard the mighty blasts and were overwhelmed with happiness. They had succeeded! Many people had remained awake to wait for the explosion, and others got up now to welcome the heroes. There was no doubt that the train had been blown up. Even in the forest they had heard it passing, and the echoes of the explosion had testified to a powerful impact. When explosives blow up without destroying anything, they do not cause such powerful echoes.

Half an hour later, Vachek reached the forest. Those who saw him cheered in his honor. Shimon was among the first to welcome him. His sharp eyes anxiously searched for Paltiel's shadow, but in vain. Shimon's heart beat faster. He approached Vachek and asked excitedly, "Where is Paltiel?"

Vachek answered, "I assume Paltiel will come in a few minutes."

"What do you mean 'in a few minutes'? Didn't you come back together?" asked Shimon.

"Germans were standing guard on top of the trains, and when they saw us they began to shoot. Each of us ran in a different direction," Vachek answered, removing his cap and showing them the visor. "There is no doubt that Paltiel will come in a little while. Perhaps he is hiding some place, or sat down to rest a bit."

Vachek's words did not convince Shimon. They left him in great despair. If Paltiel didn't come, what would be the fate of the other Jews living side by side with the Poles in the forest?

Paltiel didn't come.

‹§ 15 §› *The Poles' Distress*

The Poles saw how upset the Jews were over Paltiel, but they were not disturbed. They were happy that the exploit had been successful and that now the townspeople would praise them for their bravery. They even perceived the Jews' distress as a sign of weakness not befitting the brave of heart. They didn't see how anyone could mourn one man's death at a time like this. Even in times of peace, death did not greatly disturb them, and certainly not in wartime.

Vachek, who kept his secret to himself, tried to pretend to be sorry that his comrade, Paltiel, had not returned. But grief cannot be feigned. Vachek's attempts were not only unsuccessful; they almost gave him away. Anyone who witnessed Vachek's strange "grief" wondered. But Shimon didn't wonder; his suspicions were now confirmed. Vachek's attempts at concern only increased Shimon's grief.

But the Poles' elation over their triumph was short-lived. That very evening Yashek and Stashek went to the village to bring food and to bask in the glory of their victory. They wanted to hear what was being said in town about their exploit against the military transport.

Instead of feeling glorified, they were frustrated and

disappointed to hear all the farmers speaking about the bravery of the Jews. A Jew had been found murdered near the railway tracks, and according to all the signs it was he who had laid the explosives on the tracks and blown up the train and all its passengers. One farmer even knew that the Jew had a loaded pistol in his pocket. The farmers were awed by the bravery of the Jews. This was their second great achievement. According to the farmers, Nachrovah was like a beehive with everyone talking about the feat of the Jew who was found dead near the railway tracks.

When Yashek and Stashek returned to the forest and told their countrymen what they had heard in the village, the Poles were deeply disappointed — Vachek most of all. He had brought this shame upon his own head. If his comrades knew his secret, they would be furious with him. He had ruined their good name. Now people would say that the Poles had done nothing against the Germans, especially in contrast to the Jews.

Shimon and Peretz also went to the villages to get food, and they also heard of the bravery of the Jew who had blown up a military transport. Shimon thought to himself, "The price of Jewish honor is very high. Only by dying can a Jew gain esteem." It cannot be denied that this did bring Shimon some small measure of comfort. "Paltiel's sacrifice was accepted," he thought. "He has brought honor to the Jews of the forest and shame to the Poles. If Paltiel cannot be brought back to life, at least his death should be avenged. And even if revenge cannot be fully realized, the honor he has brought the Jews in Gentile eyes is in itself a kind of revenge on the Poles."

The tension between the two groups of partisans heightened. The Poles were angry that the Jews had stolen all the credit. Poles do not easily waive a claim to honor. It is too precious to them. It was not the Jews' fault that people spoke highly of them, but this made no difference. Anger needs no logical justification. It is always justified in its own eyes. Nor is it overly modest; nor does it hide for long. On the contrary, it seeks any excuse to burst out into the open.

Someone who needs an excuse for his anger can always find it—anywhere, any time. Nothing is easier, and the Poles soon found an excuse to release all their pent-up anger against the Jews. This is what happened:

The Poles had often seen Peretz talking privately with Chaim. At first they paid no attention, but gradually their curiosity was aroused. How long could an adult talk to a child? Once Stashek took Chaim aside, after he had left Peretz, and asked him what Peretz had been talking about. A kind of friendship had grown between Stashek and Chaim since that time that Stashek had found him asleep in the forest and had spoken to him softly. Stashek often remarked that he had already met Chaim before, but he couldn't recall when or where. This also brought the two of them together. Chaim told Stashek that Peretz had been telling him stories. Surprised, Stashek asked, "What kind of stories?"

"Peretz was telling me about Bar Kochba," Chaim answered.

"Who was Bar Kochba?"

"He was a Jewish hero who fought against the Romans who destroyed Jerusalem and burnt down the Holy Temple," answered Chaim.

All the Poles listened to the conversation between Chaim and Stashek. Among them was Vachek. Vachek jumped up as though bitten by a snake. He ran over to Peretz, who was then talking with Shimon.

"What kind of stories have you been telling the boy?" Vachek asked Peretz.

"What difference does it make to you?" replied Peretz.

Vachek said, "It's wrong to tell children lies."

"What are you talking about?" asked Peretz.

Vachek answered, "The stories about Bar Kochba are lies."

"How do you know they are lies?" asked Peretz.

"The Jews have no heroes," stated Vachek.

Shimon broke in, "They certainly do! They have always had heroes, and even today there are Jewish heroes."

"Who are the Jewish heroes of today?" challenged Vachek.

Shimon answered, "Chaim's father and Paltiel are heroes."

Shimon's reply hit Vachek where it hurt the most.

"Paltiel a hero?" he thought to himself. "I, Vachek, did the bulk of the work in exploding the train, and Shimon has the nerve to call Paltiel a hero?" The blood rose to his face. He screamed with all his might, "Jews are cowards who make themselves out to be heroes. They steal the honor of the Poles. There is good reason to dislike them." Then he raised his fist and was about to punch Shimon in the face, but Shimon was quicker, and he struck Vachek forcefully.

No one knows what might have happened next had not Peretz come between them just in time. Peretz knew that

Shimon, while fighting with a Gentile, would not let up until the Gentile was in danger of his life. Here in the forest, this would endanger all the Jews. Peretz placed himself between the two enemies and scolded them softly until they both agreed to give up the fight. The Poles, who had been watching the incident, pressed their lips together and swallowed their anger. All that day and the next, tempers ran high among the partisans. Little by little the storm settled outwardly, and only the hidden rancor in their hearts remained.

One day, the partisans heard many voices outside the forest. They were sure that these were the voices of Germans who had come to capture them. They knew that the Germans would not sit quietly by after the operation against the military train. Silence would mean surrender and would constitute an invitation to the partisans to repeat the operation. The partisans were gripped by fear. Face-to-face combat with the Germans would be very dangerous. After all, the partisans were a small group with only the poorest and smallest number of weapons. The Germans, on the other hand, had an unlimited stockpile and could send an unlimited number of soldiers to the forest. This new threat made the partisans forget about the fight between Vachek and Shimon. Now was not the time for matters of that sort. Now they must all unite to prevent the Germans from penetrating the forest.

All day long the next day, the partisans waited for the Germans to enter the forest. They prepared themselves for face-to-face combat and didn't even leave the forest to find food. Much to their astonishment, although the voices outside had not ceased, the day passed and not one German had been seen in the forest. That day, they also heard planes fly low over the forest, and there was the sound of shooting to the east, not far away. They wondered what was happening. If the planes had come to drop flares into the forest, why hadn't they done so? If the shooting was directed against the partisans, why did it sound as if it were outside the forest?

Another day passed without food from outside. People were getting hungry. Perhaps the Germans were blockading the forest in an attempt to starve the partisans out. But in that case, what did the planes and shooting have to do with the blockade? One more day went by, full of endless questions but no answers.

Then Yashek and Shimon sent some men to see what was happening. The men advanced slowly to the edge of the forest, not in a group, but singly, each one separated from the other by several hundred feet. Peretz was one of them. When the partisans got very close to the edge of the forest, they saw innumerable Germans, all coming from the east and proceeding westward.

The men ran back to the camp to tell what they had seen, but it was still puzzling. Was it possible that the Germans were really fleeing for their lives—away from the eastern front? It seemed that they were.

When the partisans heard the report about the German
retreat, they let out cries of surprise and began to move
towards the road. Everyone went to see the miracle. Hearts
beat quickly and feet were light. Yet they walked silently.
Although they had no doubt that the Germans were really
fleeing, they still had not overcome their surprise, and so
they could not fully express their happiness.

They reached the edge of the forest and with their own
eyes saw the long lines of German soldiers clearly retreating
in panic. Their eyes filled with tears, blurring their vision.
They wiped away the tears, and their hearts lightened at the
wonderful sight. They tried to see where the lines of
retreating Germans began and where they ended, but they
couldn't. The lines moved like waves in an endless sea, with
neither beginning nor end.

They gave up trying to measure the long lines stretch-
ing endlessly in both directions, and concentrated on the
Germans passing close by them. Looking closely, they saw
fear in the Germans' eyes. The Germans, in turn, saw strange
people standing along the edge of the forest, and they were
afraid of being shot. Even the guns that they carried could

not protect them from the fear in their hearts. Fear which no gun can banish accompanies fleeing soldiers.

When the partisans saw just how fearful the Germans were, they were ashamed that they had not thought of attacking them. They had been standing there like little children absorbed in watching an interesting film. Of course, it was dangerous to shoot from such a short distance. Although the Germans were afraid, they would undoubtedly defend themselves if attacked and would cause casualties among the partisans.

The partisans retreated to the forest. They sent the women and children back to the camp, and only the men remained at the site. Hiding behind trees close by, they began to fire bullets at the rows of marching Germans. The Germans panicked. Some tried to return fire, but they couldn't hit the partisans who were protected by the trees. There were many casualties among the German ranks, until they finally realized that the area was unsafe and began to detour around it. Shortly afterward, the march along the forest stopped altogether.

Now the partisans could only watch the Germans moving towards Nachrovah, out of reach of their rifles. There was no point in trying to pursue them. In the open field, the Germans would have a great advantage both in numbers and in weapons. It would be preferable to wait in the forest. Perhaps a few more Germans, not realizing the danger, would chance to pass by.

With time on their hands, they left the forest to examine the victims who had fallen on the path. They estimated a total of several hundred. Satisfaction filled their hearts. Now it couldn't be said that they had done nothing in the forest. The hundreds that they had felled were an accomplishment to be proud of.

As they were looking at the spread of German corpses lying on the ground, it seemed to Shimon that one of them was alive. He went up to the "corpse," touched his hand, and pulled him this way and that, until the "dead man" opened his eyes and looked straight into Shimon's. Shimon commanded him to stand up and he did so. All the partisans came running to watch the show. They surrounded the German, whose leg was slightly wounded. He stood forlornly, his eyes bulging. The partisans were astonished. They had never before seen such a wretched German. They were accustomed to proud, self-assured Germans, whose whole appearance proclaimed that the world was created for them alone. They had never seen a frightened German whose whole appearance proclaimed subjugation and humiliation. Standing and watching the German filled their hearts with joy. This sight alone gave them great satisfaction.

Finally, they remembered that they had to do something with this German. Yashek asked him where the soldiers were going. The German didn't answer. Yashek spoke Polish, and he, the German, couldn't understand what was being said. When he didn't answer, Yashek kicked him so hard that he fell over. Shimon remarked to Yashek, "There is no doubt that a kick like that befits a German, but he didn't understand you." When the German got to his feet, Shimon repeated Yashek's question in Yiddish, which is similar to German. The Nazi understood part of it and guessed the rest. He answered that they were fleeing from the Russians who had been pursuing them for several weeks.

From his tone of voice, it was obvious that he admired the Russians for their strength. When Shimon translated the German's answer into Polish, Stashek said, "He is a fawning bootlicker! He wants to butter us up so that we'll let him live."

Shimon answered, "It's not just bootlicking; it's also admiration. Germans admire strength. They will serve anyone who is strong."

The partisans tried to decide what to do with their captive. There was no doubt that he deserved to be killed. The only question was what type of death he deserved. The German looked into their eyes and read their thoughts. He became very nervous. He looked at the Poles, pleading for mercy with his eyes. Then he remembered the Jews among them. He had spent a lot of time learning how to recognize the Jews. His officers had also told him that Jews were soft-hearted cowards and that there was no need to fear them.

Now, when he noticed Jews among the Poles, he turned to them to save him. If they were soft-hearted, they would not be able to refuse his pleas. He looked at Shimon and was startled. He saw before him a Jew, fitting all the signs and stereotypes he had been taught, but this Jew's eyes showed no signs of a soft heart. Shimon looked into the German's eyes and read his thoughts. All the hate that had accumulated in Shimon's heart welled up in his eyes until it nearly pierced the German's heart. The German saw that he would get no mercy from this Jew. Apparently his officers had lied to him about this, just as they had lied when they had promised a fast victory over the Russians. Yes, they had fed them lies, deliberately misled them. From between clenched teeth, he let out a juicy curse. For whom? He himself didn't know.

Shimon said, "He should be hanged."

Yashek replied, "There'll be time to hang him later."

Shimon asked, "And what do you plan to do meanwhile?"

Yashek answered, "Let's have a little fun with him first. It's not every day that a German falls into our hands."

"What kind of fun?" asked Shimon.

Yashek replied, "Let's kill him limb by limb until hanging is unnecessary. We'll hang him later, as a decoration."

Shimon said, "We are not like the Germans who enjoy that kind of fun. A murderer must be put to death, but the death penalty is not for fun."

"The Jews are soft-hearted and can't stand to watch someone fluttering between life and death," said Yashek. When Shimon saw that Yashek would not give up his "fun," he left.

Shimon and his men stood a short distance away and spoke about the Germans' retreat. They said, "The end of the war is near. The world will again return to normal, and this nightmare will finally pass away. The Jews will leave the ghetto and return to their homes, and perhaps those who were taken away will also return to Nachrovah and Temyonovah. They must have withstood much torture and suffering, but time heals all wounds. Even their suffering will eventually cease." They sighed over so-and-so who had died or been killed. They sighed over the deaths of Yudel Glick,

and Zechariah the butcher, and Paltiel the porter. Shimon
was reminded of Brachah, who must be brought back from
Marussa. Someone would have to take care of Chaim, now
that his father had been killed. Who knew what had happened to his mother? If Reb Yisrael Reichman was still alive,
he would care for his grandson. But who knew if he was still
alive?

An hour later, Shimon and his men returned to the
Poles and saw the German hanging from a tree. They didn't
ask what the Poles had done to him. Shimon looked at the
German and said, "Hanging befits a German like a
cockscomb befits a rooster." The Poles looked contemp-
tuously at the Jews who had not taken part in the German's
death.

After the Germans evacuated Nachrovah, all of the partisans left the forest, and the Jews immediately returned to the ghetto. But the ghetto was empty. Not a single living soul was there. The houses were empty both of people and of any personal belongings. This was very strange. The partisans knew that the Germans' custom was to abduct the Jews, but not to touch the little that those Jews left behind them. Nor did the Germans permit the Jews to take with them more than the absolute minimum that was necessary for survival. Then what had happened to all the odds and ends that every house is full of, even in the ghetto? In many apartments only the four walls remained. Some of the houses had missing doors and windows. Here and there even the woodwork had been removed.

The Jews were deeply pained at this sight, and they were very anxious about the fate of their brothers. Shimon suggested, "You stay here in the ghetto, and Peretz and I will go to ask the Poles where all the Jews are."

In every house, the Poles opened the door only a crack. Through the crack Shimon and Peretz asked the tenants about the Jews of the ghetto, and through the crack they received their reply. Not all the householders gave the same reply. Those who were noncommittal said they didn't know. Those who were open and honest said, "All we know is that the Jews were deported from the ghetto by the Germans."

Shimon asked, "Peretz, my brother, why don't the Poles allow us to enter their houses? Are they afraid we'll burn their houses down with our fiery breath?"

Peretz answered, "They're afraid of the 'evil eye.' "

"Why are they more afraid now than they ever were before?" asked Shimon.

Peretz bent over and touched the sidepost of the door with his fingertips. When Shimon looked down to examine the spot that Peretz had touched, he saw a slanted stripe where the paint had faded. There had once been a kosher *mezuzah* in that place, guarding a Jewish home. Peretz put his hand to his mouth and kissed his fingertips. Shimon did the same. Tears were in both their eyes.

Peretz said, "If the Poles even took things which had to be uprooted from Jewish houses, they must certainly have taken everything that wasn't nailed down. That's why they don't want us in their houses. They don't want us to see those things."

At that moment, Shimon was reminded of Brachah. "Come, Peretz, my brother," he said. "Let's go find Yudel Glick's daughter."

As they passed one of the houses, Shimon stopped for a minute and looked at it. Peretz asked, "What do you see in this house that attracts your attention?"

Shimon answered, "I see something new here. This house never had a courtyard before."

Peretz examined the hedge around the yard and said, "You call this a courtyard — but I would call it a graveyard." Shimon looked at him quizzically as Peretz pointed to one of the stones in the hedge and said, "This is a gravestone." Shimon examined the stone and saw that it was straight and wide at one end, narrow and rounded at the other. He knew that Peretz was right. Shimon and Peretz went to the gate, looked inside and saw that Hebrew letters had once been engraved on the inner side of the stone. It was impossible to read the inscription, for the letters had been chiseled away, but there was enough left to see that they had been in the holy tongue.

When they reached Mr. Sokolsky's house, Stashek walked out of the door. Surprised to see him there, Shimon exclaimed, "Oh, it's you!" He hesitated a minute and then asked, "You were in the house. Did you see Mrs. Shmendrikovitz there?"

Stashek answered curtly, "This is my father's house. There is no one here by that name."

Surprised at his answer, Shimon objected, "It may be your father's house, but I was told that Mrs. Shmendrikovitz lives here."

"Who told you that?" asked Stashek.

Shimon answered, "The person who told me is no longer alive. He was Chaim's father. His daughter is in Mrs. Shmendrikovitz's care." Suddenly, Stashek had an insight. The riddle of Chaim, which had bothered him for so long, was solved.

Stashek paused a minute and then said, "Apparently the Jew who told you that was mistaken; if not, then he misled you. The Sokolsky family, not the Shmendrikovitz family, lives here. Now get out of here, Shimon, and don't disturb us."

Shimon measured Stashek from the soles of his feet to the top of his head, and said to himself, "Vachek was not the only one. They are all Jew-haters." Like many of the Jews of Nachrovah, he had never heard the name Sokolsky. Perhaps this was Yank's fault. Everyone had called Mr. Sokolsky "the father-in-law of Mr. Shmendrikovitz," until few Jews were familiar with the name Sokolsky. Shimon and Peretz left, their hopes of finding Brachah dashed.

Since they found no Jews in the ghetto of Nachrovah, they went to look for Jews in the ghetto of Temyonovah, but both towns had shared the same fate. Nor did the Poles of Temyonovah open their doors to the Jews more than a crack, through which they stared with wicked, bewildered eyes. The Jews who had returned from the forest gave up trying to find Jews from the ghetto. Apparently, the Germans hadn't wanted to leave any behind to tell what they had done to them.

There was still one glimmer of hope. Although there were no Jews left in the small towns, perhaps they could find some in the big cities. The cities offered more opportunities to hide and so to remain alive, and many more Jews had lived in the big cities; possibly a few had managed to survive. But even if they found no Jews in the cities either, they would never return to Nachrovah or Temyonovah. No Jew could live side by side with Poles who shut their doors in his face and wouldn't allow a Jew to pass their threshold. What would happen if they did find other Jews was also an open question. They only knew that if they did locate other Jews, they would do whatever these Jews did.

The group remained in Nachrovah and Temyonovah only one day. The next day, they decided to set out for Cracow. Cracow had been one of the oldest and most important Jewish communities in Poland. It was impossible to imagine Cracow without Jews.

But before leaving, the Jews went to take their leave of the dead. The Germans couldn't have banished the dead; at least *they* must have remained in their places. But when they reached the cemetery, they saw that they had been mistaken.

The Germans had also banished the dead, for even though they remained in their places, their places were unidentifiable. All the gravestones had been uprooted. With no stones on any of the graves, who could tell where anyone was buried? Grass grew over the graves, covering the dead from the eyes of the living. The living stood there, wanting to bid farewell to the dead, but not knowing what to say in parting. Should they ask for forgiveness for leaving them behind with the Poles? Heaven and earth were witness that they did so against their will, not voluntarily. They could not live together with such evil people. They also had to continue their search for the Jews from the ghetto — perhaps some of them would need their help.

Peretz stood up and said, "I have something to say to the dead." All turned their eyes to him. "In the cemetery of Nachrovah, righteous men and women of good deeds rest in peace. When the redemption comes, speedily in our days, and the *Mashiach* arrives, the dead of Nachrovah will come to Eretz Yisrael through special paths and will be resurrected.

"I beg of you, the dead of Nachrovah, in God's Name, not to forget to bring with you to Eretz Yisrael—Yudel Glick, and Paltiel the porter. They died *al kiddush haShem*, to sanctify God's Name, even though they were not privileged to be buried here with the other Jews in the cemeteries of Nachrovah and Temyonovah."

"We must all recite *Kaddish* over the Jews of the ghetto whose graves are not known," said Shimon. "And we must recite *Kaddish* beside all the graves which have been desecrated." Everyone stood up. Shimon took Chaim and stood the child beside him, saying, "Chaim is an orphan and must recite with everyone else." The men stood together and, in a loud voice, said the prayer. The women and children answered, "May His great Name be blessed forever . . ."

When the Jews reached the railway station, they found it
teeming with Poles. When their eyes met, the Poles read
much suffering in the eyes of the Jews, and the Jews read
much contempt in the eyes of the Poles. They waited a long
time for the train as in those days nothing worked very
efficiently. After the chaos of a war in which everyone was
against everyone, it was not simple to restore order.

When the train arrived, the Jews all tried to squeeze
into one empty car, together, but they could not all fit. Some
of them had to crowd into the next car together with the
Poles. The Jews all squeezed into one corner by themselves,
so as not to be together with the Poles whose eyes reflected
their displeasure. The Poles were angry and disappointed to
see so many Jews board the train. When the Germans had
left Nachrovah, the Poles were sure that there were no Jews
left in the world. They assumed the Germans had murdered
them all, but now they saw that many Jews had remained
alive. They had never dreamed so many could be saved.
Their disappointment made them bitter, but they didn't
dare express themselves out loud. Poland was under a new
regime, and the hated Russians were now on Polish soil.

Perhaps the Russians would not look favorably on open enmity towards Jews. It was better not to take chances, better to wait and see.

The train began to move. From time to time it stopped. The Jews looked through the window in their corner, searching for Jews among the crowds waiting in the station. No, there were no Jews among them. Although some passengers got off, more and more boarded at each stop, so that the cars became more and more crowded. As more Poles entered the car, the Jews were pushed even tighter into their corner. A heavy silence rested on the car, such as exists between two enemy camps who must be careful not to reveal anything to each other.

What could the Poles talk about in those days, if not about the war that was over? And how could they talk about the war without mentioning the Jews? But they were too uncomfortable to talk about them in their presence. With the opinion of the new regime as yet unknown, it was too dangerous to say some things out loud. And the Jews certainly would not talk about themselves in the presence of non-Jews. So each one kept his thoughts to himself. On the other hand, in the car where the Jews were alone, they spoke freely.

Shimon was in the car with the Poles. He wanted to be where the danger was, and there was less to worry about in the Jewish car than in the mixed car. Shimon knew how the Poles felt about the Jewish survivors, and he was prepared for anything. Some Pole might be unable to restrain himself and might come to attack one of the Jews. It was necessary to have someone among the Jews ready to fight back.

In normal times, the trip from Nachrovah to Cracow took five hours, but at that time it took six. There were fewer cars and more passengers. The passengers delayed the train in their efforts to squeeze into the already packed cars. Between one station and the next, the train traveled with breakneck speed, as if trying to make up for the delays.

It was noon. The sun beat down on the cars as the train slowed down. The Jews thought they were approaching a station and squeezed next to the window to see if there were any Jews in the station. But when they looked outside, they saw that the train was stopping in the middle of the fields opposite a small forest. Five young Poles entered the car of the Jews and commanded all the Jews to get off the train. The Jews, their hearts full of fear, didn't move. The Poles began to push them roughly towards the door. In a few seconds all the Jews in the car were standing on the tracks below.

When Shimon looked through the window of his car and saw the Jews from the adjacent car getting off, he was puzzled, and he quickly joined them. At that moment the young Poles got off and commanded the Jews to march towards the forest. Shimon, fearing tragedy, knew it was time for him to act. In a split second, he raised his hand and lowered his fist onto the skull of one of the Poles. The Pole managed to let out an "Oy" and fell to the ground. The other four Poles were so surprised, they lost their ability to think. They had expected tears and pleas for mercy from the Jews, but never blows. After all, this was not the first time they had taken Jews off the train.

Shimon knew that one was no match for five, not even

one like him, and that even if Peretz, Yonah, and the others came to his aid, there were a hundred times more Poles on the train. He would have to act quickly and not give the Poles time to think. He raised his hand again and repeated what he had done the first time. One more Pole buckled and fell. The remaining three Poles fled to the forest.

Shimon motioned to the Jews to return to their car immediately. He himself was the last one to remain on the tracks. Just then a shot was fired from the forest, and a bullet entered Shimon's head. As he fell onto the tracks, a terrifying shriek was heard from the steam engine. The train began to move, as if, terrified by Shimon's courage, it was trying to flee.

No complaints were possible against Peretz and the other Jews who had not come to Shimon's aid. Everything had happened so fast that Peretz and the others couldn't grasp it. When Peretz finally realized what happened, he sighed and said, "Happy are you, Shimon. You died a hero's death and saved a whole Jewish community. Woe to that man whose hour has not yet arrived." By "that man," Peretz meant himself. He envied Shimon and was sorry not to have been found worthy of a similar fate.

Preoccupied with their own sorrow, none of the Jews paid any attention to the reaction of the Polish passengers on the train. But we, as bystanders, noticed. When the Jews were ordered off the train, the Poles pushed their heads out the windows, broad smiles on their faces. They rubbed their hands together in eager anticipation. The minute Shimon went into action, their smiles disappeared and they clenched their fists, waiting to see what would happen. When the train left with the Jews aboard, they pulled their heads back into the cars, a disappointed look on their faces.

Before the train arrived in Cracow, Peretz said, "We must fulfill Shimon's will." They all looked at Peretz, not knowing what he was referring to. Peretz explained, "It was Shimon who said that we should recite *Kaddish* together in the graveyard of Nachrovah in memory of the Jews of the ghetto. Now we must recite *Kaddish* together, for him."

All the men, including Chaim, stood up and recited *Kaddish*, and all the women and children answered, "May His great Name be blessed." This time there were no tears in their eyes; instead, their eyes were filled with fear.

When the train reached Cracow, the Jews of the forest got off and, to their great joy, saw that there were other Jews in the train station. These Jews looked neither like partisans nor like ghetto Jews, but like pre-war Jews. But there was no time to speculate, for these strange Jews surrounded them, greeted them with warm smiles, and took them away from the station. Later, the partisans found out that these were Jews from America and from Israel.

These members of the Jewish Rescue Committee brought the partisans to a house where they had prepared everything the refugees could possibly require. They exchanged their torn clothing for new clothes. They fed them a hot meal and gave them clean beds where they might rest from the hardships that had been their lot for years.

Chaim was not the only orphan in Cracow. There were many children among the survivors, orphaned of both father and mother. The Rescue Committee grouped all the children together, apart from the adults. A child's world is different from that of an adult, and it is not wholesome for children to have no corner of their own, to always be in the company of adults. In the children's house, they resumed their studies.

The Jews of Nachrovah and Temyonovah knew that this was only a temporary station. The Rescue Committee had come to evacuate them. The soil of Poland was too soaked with Jewish blood for Jews to remain there. The remnants of the Jewish people were being gathered together in order to sail abroad. They had their choice of many possible destinations, but the most popular were Israel and America. Each person was free to choose his own destination.

Most of the Jews of Nachrovah chose Israel. Peretz chose Eretz Yisrael because it was the home of the Maccabees, Rabbi Akiva, and Bar Kochba. Others chose it because their relatives, killed by the Nazis, would be there when the dead were resurrected. For many of the partisans, this was a source of great comfort.

The orphans and the children of parents who had chosen to move to Israel were the first to be sent to Israel. Children were given preferential treatment because they needed to return to school and they had less strength to withstand suffering. The children were sent on their way by Jewish Agency and Rescue Committee representatives. The Jews of Nachrovah also accompanied them to the train station. Chaim was one of the children in this first group. After Shimon's death, Peretz had "adopted" and looked after him. Now, Peretz accompanied Chaim to the train station, going along as far as he could, and planning to meet him in the holy city of Jerusalem.

◄§ 19 §► *A Strange Walk*

On Sunday there were no classes in the convent. It was a day for recreation. The six Jewish girls never left the building to walk in the streets of Nachrovah. They only played in the yard. Through the fence they could see children running in the street, but they didn't ask why they were different from the other children. Their ghetto days had made them realize that they were different. It was a fact they simply took for granted.

One Sunday, Sarah, Rivkah, and Brachah were playing hide-and-seek together. Inside the courtyard surrounding the convent building were a few small service buildings behind which they could hide. Brachah leaned her head on the fence separating the yard from the street, her eyes closed until Sarah and Rivkah would hide and she would go to look for them. Suddenly, Brachah was startled to hear her name spoken. She opened her eyes and saw two men walking past the fence. They had already taken a few steps away from her. She looked at them and realized they were Jews. Both had beards, one black and one red. Their old worn-out clothes testified that they were from the ghetto. Brachah was bewildered. Why had they mentioned her name? Who were they? Was one of them her father? She wanted to cry "Abba," but she was afraid that if she did, Maria would be angry with her.

Sarah and Rivkah waited and waited for Brachah to come and find them, but in vain. Finally, tired of waiting, they left their hiding places and went to look for her. At the entrance to the building they saw Brachah standing in her place, not even trying to find them. Coming up to her, they asked indignantly if she had forgotten they were playing. In a voice shaking with excitement she explained to them that her father had just passed by. Sarah laughed and said, "Brachah, you are just daydreaming."

Brachah answered, "He mentioned my name."

Rivkah said, "You think about your father so much that you imagined he passed by."

"But he wasn't alone," objected Brachah. "Another Jew from the ghetto was with him. The other one had a short, red beard."

At that moment, Maria came into the yard. When the girls saw her, they stopped their conversation. Maria had sharp eyes and saw that they were telling secrets. Curious as to what they had been talking about, she thought it might be important for her to know what had been said. She came over to them and asked them, but the girls didn't answer. Sarah looked at Brachah as if to say it was up to Brachah to answer the question. Maria's curiosity was aroused. Apparently this was an important secret. She asked them again what they were talking about, but in place of an answer, Brachah burst into tears. Maria was taken by surprise.

In a stiff, dry voice, she turned a third time to Sarah, the eldest of the three, to tell her what was happening. Sarah's eyes turned towards Brachah's, and Maria read in them an apology. Then Sarah turned to Maria and told her of the newest incident with Brachah. For a minute, Maria was taken aback. She knew that Jewish partisans had indeed come back from the forest and were walking around town. Two of them could have passed by. Could one of them have been Brachah's father? But hadn't Brachah's father been killed over a year ago in the explosion of the Gestapo headquarters? Either Brachah had been mistaken then, or she was mistaken now. Perhaps this was all witchcraft as Tzorerkeh had told her then.

Knowing that she had to say something, Maria scolded the girls for talking nonsense and immediately returned to the convent. Inside, she told her friends of the incident with Brachah. Sinavkeh advised, "The girls should be kept inside and not permitted in the yard. There are Jews all over town, and perhaps they are looking for the girls." Tzorerkeh agreed with Sinavkeh. Maria went out to the yard and called the girls into the house. Today they would play inside. The girls lowered their eyes, knowing that this was their punishment for talking nonsense.

The following Sunday, Maria told the girls that they would go for a walk through the town. The girls broke out in exclamations of astonishment. They had never dared to hope for such a thing. How wonderful! A minute later, Rivkah hesitatingly asked Maria, "Really, Maria?—or are you just joking?"

Maria repeated herself in a holiday tone of voice, "Today—and not only today, but every day from now on — the girls may take walks and play in the streets of the town, not only in the yard." The girls were overjoyed. They didn't know what had caused the change, and they didn't want to ask. Whatever it was, was for the good. In the afternoon — in just another two hours — they would walk through the streets.

At dinner, the girls had no appetite. Their great expectations made them forget about food. Maria understood and did not rebuke them for eating carelessly.

At 2:00 PM, the six girls left the convent. Two nuns, Sinavkeh and Tzorerkeh, accompanied them on their walk. Maria didn't go with them this time. When they were in the street, the nuns paused, and Sinavkeh asked the girls, "Where do you want to go?"

The girls looked at each other and didn't answer. Sinavkeh repeated the question. Brachah whispered, "Perhaps we could go to the ghetto."

"Very well," answered Sinavkeh. "Let's go to the ghetto. Anywhere you like."

The girls stopped chattering and walked silently beside the nuns. Their hearts were beating strongly. What would happen if they met their fathers and mothers in the ghetto? After a long silence, Sarah stopped for a minute, turned to the nuns, and asked in bewilderment, "Will we be allowed to leave the ghetto? I know that no one is allowed to leave the ghetto."

Sinavkeh and Tzorerkeh smiled, and Tzorerkeh said, "Now everyone can leave the ghetto." Sarah didn't quite understand. If it were now permitted to leave the ghetto, why hadn't her father and mother come to get her?

Nevertheless she didn't ask any more questions. She realized that this was a very complicated matter which was not easily understood.

As they drew near the ghetto gate, they saw that it was open and unguarded. The girls looked at it cautiously, not comprehending how the ghetto gate could be left unguarded. They walked down the main street of the ghetto, Katlinskah Street, looking searchingly in all directions. They saw no one. They walked up and down a few more streets and still saw no one. Rivkah asked, "Can we go into the houses?"

"Certainly," answered Sinavkeh, "let's go into the houses. We'll go wherever you want." They went into one house, a second house, a third. All the houses were empty.

As they passed one house, Sarah jumped up and called out happily, "This is our house! I want to go into our house." They all went into the house. It was deserted. Not a living soul was inside. Sarah asked Sinavkeh in a desperate tone, "Where are all the Jews?"

Sinavkeh answered, "Come girls, let's leave this house. Outside I will explain everything."

Once outside, Sinavkeh and Tzorerkeh sat the girls on a pile of stones near the house. Tzorerkeh pointed to the pile they were sitting on and said, "This pile is all that remains of a house that was destroyed in the war between the Poles and the Germans. Before the Germans fled, the Poles bombed this house and destroyed it. Many houses were destroyed during the war and many people were killed. There are no more Jews in the ghetto because before the Germans fled, they killed all the Jews."

Tzorerkeh's speech frightened and confused the girls.

"Where are my father and mother?" asked Sarah.

"And mine?" asked Rivkah.

"And mine?" asked Brachah.

Tzorerkeh repeated, "I don't know where your fathers and mothers are. I only know that the Germans killed all the Jews they found in the ghetto."

"That's not true," said Brachah. "I saw my father near our house on Catholichka Street last Sunday."

Sinavkeh answered, "Maybe it wasn't a Jew that you saw, and if it was, perhaps he wasn't from Nachrovah. It certainly wasn't your father. There are no Jews from Nachrovah left."

Brachah answered, "There were two of them, not one. One was my father."

Tzorerkeh said, "Brachah, you're talking like a baby." Brachah was embarrassed and said nothing further.

Sarah asked, "Why did the Germans kill all the Jews?"

Tzorerkeh answered, "This was their punishment from Heaven."

"For what?" asked Sarah.

Tzorerkeh answered, "This was their punishment for denying that Jesus was the Messiah."

When Tzorerkeh mentioned Jesus, Brachah knew that she was talking about the little boy in the picture with his mother. She couldn't understand what the Jews wanted from the boy. Such a poor, little boy. Brachah was sorry for him and ashamed of her parents for denying him. She didn't understand what the word "denying" meant, but when Tzorerkeh had spoken about it, Brachah had understood that it was something bad. They certainly didn't like him — but why, she didn't understand.

After that, the girls returned to the convent. At night, when they kneeled before the picture of the mother and the child, they couldn't look at the child's eyes. They felt guilty. Their fathers and mothers had denied him. At that moment they forgot that their fathers and mothers were among the Jews that the Germans had killed, as Tzorerkeh had told them today. The girls only remembered that their parents had denied Jesus and they were sorry for it. They lowered their eyes and couldn't look at the picture.

From that day on, the girls went wherever they wanted to in the streets of Nachrovah, and they played outside with all the other children. They were also given new names. Brachah was called Barbara.

One day, Maria announced that today the girls would be baptized as Catholics. They were overjoyed. They didn't know what baptism was, but they knew that afterwards they would be different than they were now, and they were curious to know just how they would be different. They also knew that after baptism they would no longer have to be ashamed of the Jews denying Jesus. They would be able to look straight at the picture and not have to lower their eyes during prayers.

The girls were brought to Nachrovah's Catholic church. Many people came to see the young Jewesses baptized. Marussa was among them. She felt personally involved, for it was she who had brought Brachah to the convent, and she was proud of herself. This accomplishment would help obliterate the bad reputation she and Yanka had acquired.

Catholics knew how to forgive. If she could show that she was a good Catholic, all would be forgiven, even her marriage to Yank.

The ceremony was short. As there were no other Jews left in Nachrovah, it no longer seemed so important to dramatize it. The priest sprinkled the girls with holy water and recited a prayer. When the girls left the church, old ladies kissed them. Marussa gave Brachah a present and asked Brachah to accept her family name. From now on, her name would be Barbara Sokolsky. The girls knew that now they were Catholic, not Jewish. They were different. Truth to tell, they were a bit disappointed. Somehow, they had thought that being different would be more exciting.

◄§ 20 ₴► *Chaim in Eretz Yisrael*

When Chaim reached Eretz Yisrael, he was placed in a Youth Aliyah school where Torah and other religious studies were taught. Chaim threw himself into his studies and in a short time his teachers noticed his talents. His intelligence and diligence gave them great hopes for him. The teachers appreciated his talents, but they esteemed him even more for his diligence. Talent is a gift fom God; one cannot choose to be talented. But diligence is a matter of choice. It is a habit which is acquired and retained only through hard work, and one who works to achieve it is worthy of esteem.

Chaim's teachers thought his diligence was due to his desire to make up for what he had missed in the ghetto and in the forest. We know that there was also another reason. Chaim had not forgotten Brachah. He hoped to find Brachah when he left the forest, but now that he was in Eretz Yisrael and Brachah was still in Nachrovah, how would he ever find her? This caused him great pain. To take his mind off Brachah and to lessen his pain, he immersed himself in his studies.

During the day, Chaim could forget about Brachah by fleeing to his books. But at night, in bed, he couldn't take

refuge in his books, and memories of Brachah would torment him. He knew that he would not be able to help her
while he was still young. Shimon was gone and there was no
one to advise him. No one here knew the slightest bit about
what had happened in Nachrovah. Maybe Yonah would
come and bring him some news about Brachah. Maybe he
would find her in Cracow. Of course, this was not very
probable. Brachah had remained in Nachrovah, so how could
Yonah find her in Cracow? Nevertheless, maybe a miracle
would happen. Maybe Brachah would come to Cracow and
Yonah would see her walking down the street. However,
Chaim knew that Yonah was not Shimon. Even if he found
her in Cracow, he might not know how to bring her to
Israel — but Chaim wanted to believe in some miracle. He
didn't want to give up his sister.

Maybe Peretz would find her and bring her to Eretz
Yisrael. Peretz was as astute as Shimon. True, Peretz didn't
know Brachah, for he was from Temyonovah, not from
Nachrovah, but Chaim knew that he and Brachah looked
very much alike. Anyone who knew him would recognize
Brachah.

Often, Brachah would take pity on her brother and visit
him in his dreams. She would smile at him, and he would
feel that she, too, was waiting for a miracle. But sometimes
she would look at him mockingly as if to tease him and say,
"You'll *never* find me again!" Then Chaim would wake up
greatly distressed. Would he really never find her? Those
were the times when Chaim would hurry to school and
drown himself in his books to relieve his distress.

When Chaim had arrived in Israel he had been placed in

third grade. Now, only three years later, he was about to finish eighth grade. By the end of the school year he would be *bar mitzvah.* The principal of the school, Mr. Avichail, was preparing a joint *bar mitzvah* celebration for five of his students. They had no fathers or mothers to care for them, and so various institutions were taking care of their needs.

There was much to do. Five good pairs of *tefillin* must be bought, and a dinner, which cost even more than the *tefillin*, must be held. The boys also needed new clothes. As they were the guests of honor, everyone's eyes would be on them and if they didn't have nice clothes, they would be very embarrassed.

Mr. Avichail received some generous donations, bought what was needed, and made all the necessary preparations. But he did not work alone; all the teachers helped him. Chaim's teacher, Mr. Melamed, taught Chaim his *bar mitzvah* speech. Of the five boys, Chaim alone would present a speech. The other boys were not as advanced as Chaim nor were they as talented. It was hard for them to make up for the years they had lost in the ghetto.

Many people were invited to the party: the local rabbi, representatives of the institutions, and many guests. Chaim must be well prepared, both for his own sake and to uphold the school's honor. Mr. Melamed was lucky; it was easy to teach Chaim. After one or two rehearsals, the boy knew the whole speech by heart.

The day of the party arrived. Rows of tables and chairs were set up along the whole length of the school auditorium. The head table stood along the east wall. The five boys would sit in the middle and the local rabbi, a man of imposing appearance, would sit at their right with Mr. Avichail at their left. The hall filled with guests, and every seat was taken. Pupils of the school — some before and some after their own *bar mitzvah* — sat at a separate table.

Mr. Avichail rose and delivered the opening speech. He welcomed the rabbi and the other guests. Then he introduced Chaim who would deliver the *bar mitzvah* speech on behalf of all the *bar mitzvah* boys. Chaim rose and began to recite the speech Mr. Melamed had taught him. Mr. Melamed stood behind him, holding the text of the speech, ready to prompt him if, God forbid, Chaim forgot a line. There was no need to expect any trouble, for Chaim had an excellent memory, and the teacher knew that Chaim knew his speech backwards and forwards. Nevertheless, it didn't pay to take chances. Chaim was still young and could not be depended on completely.

Chaim began his speech according to the text. He spoke in a loud, clear voice, and Mr. Melamed followed his words in the text with great satisfaction. Suddenly, Chaim deviated from the text. Mr. Melamed, surprised, tried to correct him. He began to whisper more and more loudly, but Chaim didn't pay any attention. Mr. Melamed nudged Chaim gently to return to the written text of the speech. He was afraid that Chaim would get lost completely and would not know how to end the speech, and what could be worse than that!

But Chaim continued to deliver his own speech. When Mr. Melamed lost all hope of returning Chaim to the written text, he began to listen to what Chaim was saying. Apparently the boy had prepared his own speech independently, and Mr. Melamed found that it was a pleasure to listen to him. When Chaim finished, there was much applause. He had made a great impression. Even what he had read from the text had become his own, because he had put his own heart and soul into it.

Next, the rabbi spoke. He praised the *bar mitzvah* boys, and he praised Chaim's speech. Mr. Avichail was quite pleased that the speech Mr. Melamed had written found favor in the rabbi's eyes. After the rabbi had finished talking, Mr. Melamed — a modest person — told Mr. Avichail the whole story, and Mr. Avichail related it to the rabbi. He was quite impressed. "Really?" he said. "Why, that's unbelievable!" Chaim was sitting in the middle, two boys to his right and two to his left, and did not hear the conversation between the three men. If he had, he might have blushed.

The following year Chaim entered a *yeshivah* in Jerusalem. Here he found great opportunities for his diligence. In school there had been fixed hours for each subject, which the pupils had to follow. The *yeshivah* was different. Here no one objected if he kept to one subject for many hours. Chaim began to devote himself to the study of *gemara*, to dive into the deep waters of the Talmud. His talents found a fertile field as his memory recorded page after page. When he learned one page, it did not make him forget the ones he'd learned before. All the pages stood in order before his eyes, even with his *gemara* closed. He was able to connect one page to the other and to bind many pages into one in his mind's eye.

During those days he almost forgot about Brachah, not only by day, but even by night. His brain was always occupied with Torah thoughts, even upon retiring, and these left no room for anything else. Nevertheless, it cannot be said that he forgot her completely. On the contrary, he tried now to keep himself from forgetting her. Once, he had fled to his books in order to relieve his heartache and to forget about Brachah for a while. Now he had to purposely remind himself of her. He must remember her. Perhaps the miracle which would reunite them would still occur.

The older he grew, the better he comprehended Brachah's tragedy. When he was little, he had longed for her because she was his only sister. Now that he was grown, he realized that Brachah was in danger, not physically but spiritually. A Jewish girl surrounded by non-Jews was liable to forget her God. Even if she remembered, how could she remain Jewish? How could one lone girl retain her Jewishness in a completely Gentile world?

Now he knew that both his father and his mother had been murdered by the Nazis. He had heard about his mother's conduct, and he understood that his father had also agreed with her course of action. She had died *al kiddush haShem*, to sanctify the Holy Name.

Would Brachah, whose mother had died because she was a Jew, become a Christian? Could there be any tragedy greater than that? Would Brachah, whose father had been so learned — a real *talmid chacham* — and more righteous than most, assimilate among the Christians? No, it was impossible to accept. Although he did not yet know what to do to save Brachah, he knew that he must not despair. His heart told him that he would find her yet.

His hopes were not without basis. In the *gemara* he had

learned about an incident that had happened to the daughter
of Rabbi Nachunya the well-digger. (Rabbi Nachunya dug
wells for the Jews who came up to Jerusalem during the
holidays, as Rashi explains.) "She fell into a deep well her
father had dug. Men came to tell Rabbi Chaninah ben Dosa.
The first time they came, he said 'Shalom.' The second time,
he said, 'Shalom.' The third time, he cried, 'She has come
out.' He asked her, 'My daughter, who took you out?' She
answered, 'A ram came along, led by an old man.' They said
to him [to Rabbi Chanina], 'You are a prophet.' He answered
them, 'I am neither a prophet nor the son of a prophet, but I
know that if a righteous man does a *mitzvah*, his children
cannot be hurt by it.' " (*Yevamoth* 121)

Chaim thought, "The same is true of Brachah. She will
not forget that she is Jewish. She will not fail in that very
thing for which both her mother and father died." He was
convinced that Brachah would remain part of the Jewish
people, but he didn't yet know how.

Brachah also grew, both in age and ability. She graduated
from school with honors. She was a devout Catholic, more
devoted than her Catholic friends who had been born into
their faith. She felt that it was up to her to receive absolution
for the sins of her heretic parents and that she could achieve
this by her devotion to Christianity.

A few weeks ago, the bishop had inquired about Sarah,
whose name was changed to Silvana. She had a brother who
had survived the war and gone to Eretz Yisrael. The Chief
Rabbi of Eretz Yisrael had come to Poland to request the
bishop's aid in returning Sarah to Judaism. Silvana was
shocked. She didn't want to return to the heretic Jews. She
wanted to be a Catholic. Barbara, however, was left in peace.
She took this to be proof that her brother also was killed by
the Germans.

She was happy that none of her Jewish relatives came
to disturb her. Nevertheless, she couldn't forget her father
and mother. She wanted to, but she couldn't. As if to make
her angry, they kept appearing before her eyes.

Barbara tried not to look in the mirror. When she
looked at herself, she was reminded of her mother. She

looked just like her. Frightened, she would look at her own eyes and see that they were black, just like her mother's. They were Jewish eyes. How happy she would have been had she been able to exchange her dark eyes for blue ones, like those of Marussa or Maria. She had been given Marussa's family name, Sokolsky, but she didn't look at all like them. What good was a Polish name if her eyes betrayed her?

Of course she didn't hate her mother. Her mother had been born Jewish, and no one could blame her for not being a Christian. But she, Brachah, didn't want to be like her mother. She was a Christian, not a Jew, and she wanted to look like one.

Years passed. Barbara successfully completed the Catholic Theological Seminary. What would she do now? This question troubled her and her teachers. After much discussion they came to the conclusion that she should act as a missionary to the Jews.

Because she looked Jewish, Jewish children would believe her more easily. She was very devout, and her talks would be most effective because they came straight from her heart. And most important of all, she must gain absolution for the sin of having been born Jewish. She could do this by bringing the children of heretics into the Catholic Church.

For years there had not been such a golden opportunity to save the souls of heretics. All the Jewish communities had been utterly destroyed by the Nazis, and the few Jews who survived were suspended between heaven and earth. They could not find their place. None of their former Christian homelands were willing to take them back, so they wandered from place to place until many of them sank into despair. If the Church were willing to help them, they could be ready to believe in Jesus. People will pay any price to find sustenance and peace.

Barbara began to work as a teacher in a mission school. She spoke to desperate, unfortunate women with no bread to feed their children — women who had wandered from place to place searching for husbands who had been lost in the stormy war. These women could be persuaded to enroll their children in the institution where Barbara taught. When Barbara saw the fear in these women's eyes, she would speak softly to them and reveal her secret, that she too had been born a Jew. She spoke in Yiddish, and this reinforced their trust in her.

The question must be asked, how had Barbara managed to remember her Yiddish after so many years among the Christians? In her dreams, she had spoken only Yiddish with her brother Chaim. Her dark eyes also spoke for her. Both Barbara's eyes and her message helped these women — and men, too — to take the step they so dreaded. The Holocaust had caused confusion in many hearts, and had implanted the seeds of disbelief. One word for or against could be decisive — and this word was often provided by Barbara.

Barbara was not alone in her work. What she did in one place, Silvana did in another. Possibly Rivkah, whose name had been changed to Cariba, was also employed as a missionary. Barbara knew that each one of her old friends from the convent was in a different place, but she was too busy to keep in touch or even to follow their activities.

At that time, a convention of priests and monks was

held to discuss recent events in the Holy Land. The Jews had proclaimed their own state, and when the seven neighboring Arab countries had tried to conquer the country, they had been defeated by the Jews. Now the country was in Jewish hands.

The Christian priests and monks were apprehensive as to what was taking place in the Holy Land. In their Sunday sermons they had always preached that the Jews were cursed and doomed to wander all their lives because they had denied the Messiah and crucified him. Now, with a Jewish state, there was no need for them to wander any longer. What would the priests say in their Sunday sermons? The priests also feared that all the boys and girls who had converted to Christianity during the Holocaust would begin to reflect about recent events in the Holy Land, and sinful thoughts are the greatest sins of all.

Some of the priests and monks were almost in despair, but to others the picture was not so bleak. "On the contrary," they said, "in the State of Israel, the mission can accomplish more than anywhere else. Everywhere else the Christians hate the Jews, and even Jewish converts do not have an easy time. When the Germans invaded the countries of Europe, they drew no distinction between Jews who had converted to Christianity and those who had not. Even converts were banished to the ghetto together with all the other Jews and sent to concentration camps with them.

"Anti-Semitism strengthens the Jews' ties to their religion. In the Holy Land, the situation is different. There, the Jews have their own state. There are no Christians to hate the Jews, so the Jews will accept the New Testament willingly, if the missionaries only find the proper way to present it to them.

"Many Jews in Israel have not yet found their places. Their state cannot offer all of them housing, food, and employment. If someone else offers these things to them, they will follow him. It is also possible to utilize the Church's connections with other countries to aid Jews in emigrating from the Holy Land. The great advantage to this is that it means one more Jew who believes in Jesus and one less Jew in the Holy Land."

This opinion gained wide circulation. Perhaps because they truly believed in it or perhaps because it was the only alternative to failure. It is human nature to do everything possible to avoid failure. By a great majority, the priests decided to embark on a great Christian mission to the Holy Land. The Holy Land in the hands of heretic Jews would endanger Christianity and its teachings. If successful, the mission would save the Jews from heresy, and the Holy Land from the Jews. The mission, which even in normal times did not suffer from a lack of funds, made special efforts to assure an unlimited amount of money for this particular campaign. They wanted to make sure they had sufficient money to attract people whose suffering had passed all limits, and there was no lack of such Jews in the Holy Land.

The clergymen pored over their lists of missionaries, choosing the most successful to be sent to the Holy Land. When they reached Barbara's name, they paused to consider whether it would be wise to send her or not. On the one hand, Barbara, with her Yiddish speech and Jewish eyes, would draw many Jews who might otherwise hesitate to convert. On the other hand, Barbara herself might return to her people once she saw that they had a state of their own.

After weighing the alternatives, they decided to send her. There was no real danger that Barbara might return to Judaism. She was a devout Christian — heart and soul — strong enough to draw other Jews after her, and not to be drawn after them. When they reached Silvana's name, they weighed the matter well and decided not to send her to the Holy Land. Silvana was not Barbara. She was not as serious and could not be relied upon so completely. She might well change her mind if she changed her residence.

When Barbara was informed of the decision to send her to the Holy Land, she was very happy. She couldn't understand why, but she was. She wondered what there was to be happy about. What difference did it make where she was working for the mission? Was saving a heretic's soul in Poland any less important than saving such a soul in the Holy Land? Nevertheless, she felt elated.

But she had little time to think about this. In a few weeks she was scheduled to leave Poland. The major arrangements, such as the trip itself, were to be taken care of by the Church, but she had many minor details to arrange for herself.

Before her trip, Barbara paid one last visit to Marussa. She had Marussa to thank for bringing her to the convent in Nachrovah and for the gift of the name, Sokolsky. She wanted to bid farewell to Marussa, and to Yanka, who had grown into a young lady. Marussa greeted Barbara warmly. When she heard that Barbara was on her way to the Holy Land as a missionary, she became reflective.

"Marussa, what are you thinking about?" Barbara asked. "I am happy, but you seem to have second thoughts."

Marussa answered, "You have been given a sacred task. I hope you are successful." Truth to tell, Marussa couldn't tell Barbara what she was thinking. She was filled with doubt as to whether it was really wise for the Church to send Barbara to the Holy Land. She, Marussa, didn't have much faith in converts. She knew that her Yank had been a convert; nevertheless he had not believed in Jesus. Who knew if Barbara's heart was true to her mouth, and even if she was sincere today, who could guarantee that she wouldn't change her mind tomorrow? Marussa, however, told Barbara nothing of the thoughts that ran through her mind.

Barbara bid farewell to Marussa and Yanka. As she took Yanka's hand, she looked into her eyes and felt a twinge of jealousy. Yanka, whose father was Jewish, nonetheless, had Polish eyes. How fortunate for her! Marussa and Yanka accompanied her to the street, said goodbye again, and returned home.

When Barbara was left alone, she stood still for a minute, deciding where to go. Then she turned towards the ghetto. As she passed the house where she and Chaim, Abba and Imma, and her grandparents had once lived, she stopped for a minute and gazed at the house. It had been changed completely — repaired and repainted. She had a great desire to see the house from the inside, but other people lived there now. What would she tell them when she entered? She wanted to go away, but desire to see the house from the inside was too strong. She found an excuse and went in.

When she entered, she apologized to the old woman she found there for disturbing her. She said she had simply made a mistake and confused this house with another. Before she left, she looked hastily around the room in which she was standing. She looked at the corner where she had lived in her ghetto days. She seemed to see a little girl. Looking into the little girl's eyes, she recognized herself. How different she was today! After apologizing to the old woman again, she left the house, but the little girl was still before her eyes. She began to walk fast, to chase the picture of the girl from her mind, but she was unsuccessful. She felt uneasy. This little girl was Jewish, but she herself was Catholic. She was not that little girl grown up. No, now she was someone else entirely.

৶ 22 ৶ *Barbara in Jerusalem*

It was Barbara's second day in Jerusalem. She had joined the teaching staff of the mission of St. Paul's Convent, where she would also live. On her first day she had rested up, after the long trip by land and sea from Nachrovah, and had not even left her new home.

On the second day, she went out to see the city. She would not begin her work for a few days. First she must get to know the people and learn how to differentiate between the different Jewish ethnic groups by their facial characteristics, language and clothing. She also needed to refresh her memory of the square Hebrew letters which she had forgotten with the years. Most important, she had to feel at home before beginning her work. In order to persuade others, she must first gain confidence in herself—which she could only do by being familiar with her surroundings.

Barbara didn't go out by herself. Paulina—also a teacher in the mission school of St. Paul's Convent—went with her. Paulina was from Germany, but they spoke French together. They had both learned the language at the Christian Theological Seminary.

On Yaffo Street, Paulina pointed to men with long

coats, sideburns and beards, and said, "Those are Jews."
Paulina knew that Barbara came from Poland. In Poland
after the war, there were very few Jews, and the few who had
remained did not look Jewish. The fear which had been
implanted in their hearts during the Holocaust had
remained, and they tried to hide by looking like Poles.

Probably, Paulina reasoned, Barbara had never before
seen a Jew with a beard and *peyoth* and a long coat in the
summer. Barbara looked at the men Paulina had pointed to,
but didn't say anything. Paulina looked into Barbara's eyes
and saw that she was preoccupied. She didn't know if she
had even heard what was said to her, or if she had noticed
the men.

At that minute a tall young man with a coal-black beard
passed by them. Barbara stopped in her tracks, turned her
head, and looked him. When he entered one of the houses,
Barbara turned around and resumed her walk. Paulina asked,
"Why did the sight of that young man make you turn
around? He's not the only one who looks like that. Here in
Jerusalem there are many more like him. They are among
the greatest heretics of all." Barbara looked into Paulina's
eyes but did not answer.

Paulina continued, "Barbara, you are as white as chalk.
What happened? Did that Jew frighten you? There is no
reason to be afraid of them. They won't do anything to us.
They do hate the mission, but they won't harm us. The law
forbids it. There is even talk that this city may no longer
remain part of the Jewish State. This city is holier to us than
it is to the Jews, and we will not relinquish it."

Paulina continued to talk for a long time, forgetting

that in the beginning she had asked Barbara a question which had not yet been answered. Paulina saw that Barbara was absorbed in her thoughts and attributed it to the fact that she was overwhelmed by the strange-looking people she had seen.

From Yaffo Street they reached Me'ah She'arim. They passed a one-story house which had a window open. Through the window came the melodious sound of someone learning *gemara*. Barbara stopped not far from the window. Paulina said, "That is how Jews study the Talmud. They don't study it; they sing it. Did you ever in your life see a man reading a book as if he's in prayer? Strange people. The Talmudists are the greatest heretics of all. There is hatred of the Christians in the Talmud. You know that in Spain, and later in Germany, the Christians burned the Talmud. Even so, it has survived until today; the Jews will not abandon it. I myself have never studied the Talmud, but I have heard from pious Christians that it is full of treachery and heresy towards Christianity."

Barbara stood and listened to the joyous voice of the Jew learning *gemara*. Suddenly, she felt sick. Leaning against Paulina, she said, "I am dizzy. I can't stand up." Paulina held Barbara and looked around for a taxi to return to the convent, but there was none. Near the house was a bench. Paulina supported Barbara, and with great difficulty, Barbara dragged herself to the bench and collapsed. Paulina was frightened by the look on Barbara's face. The voice of the Jew still reached their ears. Barbara leaned her head on Paulina's shoulder and said, "I feel a bit better. Let me just sit here for a minute."

In a while Barbara stood up and said in a slightly shaky voice, "Come, Paulina, let's go home." But before they left, she walked to the window of the house and looked into the room. Suddenly the voice stopped, and a young man with a big book in front of him looked up, surprised to see a young woman standing at the window. Barbara was frightened by his bewildered look, and she quickly drew away.

As they left Me'ah She'arim, Paulina commented, "Apparently you've never heard a Jew studying Talmud. Was it such a novelty that you had to go up to the window to see? I have heard them so many times that it no longer interests me."

When they returned to the convent, the nuns and teachers wanted to ask Barbara what she thought of the city, but when they saw her pale face, they asked no questions. No one could understand what had happened to Barbara Sokolsky.

After Barbara retired to the room she shared with Paulina, the nuns asked Paulina about Barbara. But Paulina knew no more than they did. She said, "Apparently Barbara was overwhelmed by what she saw. The new impressions had a bad effect on her." At suppertime, Paulina went to the room to see how Barbara was feeling and to bring her to the dining hall. Barbara asked to be excused. She couldn't join them for supper as she was dizzy and wanted to rest until the next morning. No, there was no need to summon a doctor. She was sure that it would pass. Paulina wished her good night and left the room quietly.

That night Barbara saw many things. As soon as she shut her eyes, she found herself standing near a low house with one open window, a sweet joyous sound emanating from it. This time, when she went up to the window and looked inside, she saw her father. Yes, it was her father. She recognized him immediately. His beard was black, his face gentle and pale. She wanted to cry "Abba" but she didn't. She was afraid he would see her and be angry with her. She didn't know why he should be angry with her, but she was afraid just the same. But then her father looked out the window and saw her. He stopped learning. The wrinkles in his high forehead relaxed, and a wide smile spread across his face. "Come in, Brachah," he said. "Why are you standing outside? It's cold at night in Yerushalayim. Inside it's warm. Come, Brachah. Come into the room."

Barbara was ashamed to look into her father's good eyes, and she turned her head to the right. There she saw her Imma. Her face was very beautiful. Barbara looked into her mother's eyes. Black eyes. Barbara sighed. Why didn't her mother have blue eyes like those of Maria and Marussa? Her mother's eyes were velvet, soothing, but so very sad. Why were they so sad? She couldn't bear to look at such sad eyes.

She turned her head to the left. There stood Chaim, grown up, tall and good-looking, a black beard adorning his handsome face. When their eyes met, Chaim asked her, "Why don't you come into the house, Brachah? Didn't Abba tell you to come in?" Barbara heard the angry note in Chaim's voice, angry because she had not listened to Abba. Barbara was not hurt by Chaim's anger. He was no older than she, and she didn't have to listen to him. After all, they were the same age.

Just then someone grabbed her shoulders. Barbara

trembled. She wanted to scream but was so afraid she couldn't utter a sound. She turned her head around and saw Grandma Leah. Her grandmother smothered her face with kisses and then entered the house. Barbara watched her.

Suddenly Barbara realized that Chaim had left the room to fetch her and bring her inside to Abba and Imma. Panic-stricken, Barbara fled as fast as she could. She ran so fast she grew short of breath.

Barbara pulled the blanket off her head and inhaled deeply. Shaken, she looked around the room and tried to remember where she was. Her dream was still very much alive. She closed her eyes, trying to recall every detail, but when she looked through the window again, the room was empty.

No Abba, no Imma, no Chaim, no Grandma Leah. Her eyes searched the corners of the room — perhaps she would catch sight of them even if they were hiding from her. In one corner, Chaim was sitting before a large book and studying. Barbara cried, "Chaim."

Chaim lifted his eyes from the book and looked at her. He said, "It's not nice, Brachah, it's not nice. Why didn't you come inside to Abba and Imma? You only have one father and one mother. If you run away from them, you will lose your footing in this world. You shouldn't run away from your brother, either. Why did you run away?"

Just then Brachah heard footsteps and knew that they were coming to get her, to bring her to Abba and Imma. She was so frightened she began to scream.

Paulina touched her lightly and said, "Barbara, why are you screaming?" Barbara opened her eyes and saw that there was no one there but Paulina. "You must have been dreaming, Barbara," said Paulina.

Barbara nodded, "Yes, I was dreaming."

Paulina held Barbara's hand tightly and said, "Dreams are full of nonsense." Then she left the room and Barbara got up.

All that day Barbara was absorbed in reflecting on what she had seen in town and later in her dreams. She knew that she must overcome her emotions. These emotions were signs of weakness, and must pass quickly. They had come to her through her encounters with Jews, but she must remain stalwart and strong. She was a Catholic, not a Jew. She must forget her parents and her brother. They had remained Jews, denying Jesus. She had been sent to the Holy Land to redeem sinful souls from heresy and not to become preoccupied herself with sinful thoughts. She must not allow herself such sinful longings. No, she would not allow these heretical thoughts to enter her heart. She would be strong. She would fulfill her mission faithfully. In a few days, Barbara recovered and began her work as a teacher in the mission school of St. Paul's Convent.

✦ 23 ✦ *From Nachrovah to Israel*

The remnants of the Jewish communities of Nachrovah and Temyonovah remained in Cracow and waited. A few immigrated to America, but most of them wanted to immigrate to Israel. The British Mandate was in force in Palestine, and few Jews were permitted to enter the country. Young orphans were allowed to immigrate, so Chaim could enter but Peretz and Yonah had to remain in Cracow.

Time passed, and some of the Jews from Nachrovah who had not been with the partisans in the forest reached Cracow. The Jews from the forest surrounded them and asked where they had been taken to and where they had spent the remainder of the war. The ghetto Jews told the partisans the following story.

One day the Germans took all the Jews from the ghetto and commanded them to start walking. They walked until they reached the forest. Then they were commanded to dig a long, deep ditch. The Jews dug the ditch, not knowing what it was for. When the ditch was ready, the German commander summoned Mr. Shefler, the head of the Jewish Committee. Mr. Shefler approached the commander and stood at attention before him. The commander said, "I would like to thank Mr. Shefler, head of the Jewish Committee, for his faithful service on behalf of the German cause. All the Jews must follow Mr. Shefler's example." Mr. Shefler blushed at the commander's words and saluted him. The commander smiled and said, "Now Mr. Shefler will do as I command him, and everyone else will follow his example."

The officer commanded Mr. Shefler to stand at the edge of the ditch, facing the ditch. Mr. Shefler quickly followed the command, but the other Jews were in no hurry to do likewise. The commander began to scream at them at the top of his voice.

Some of the German soldiers and their Polish assistants began to hit the Jews on the head with the butts of rifles and to push them towards the ditch. A number of people, especially women and children, were killed during this attack. Those who were not killed were forcibly pushed to the edge of the pit. Those who remembered the *viduy* — the confession before death — by heart, recited it aloud. Those who couldn't recall the words thought about it in their hearts.

Suddenly a shot was heard. When they turned their heads to see whom the Germans had shot, they saw Mr. Shefler fall into the pit, face first. A great tumult arose. Most people were rooted to the ground, in terror, but some started to run. Those who didn't run away fell into the pit, one by one, after Mr. Shefler. Those who fled hid in the forest. Most of them survived for only two or three days at most. No one can live on air, and they dared not approach any settlement to get provisions.

But a few Jews survived for another two or three days, until the Russians entered Nachrovah. Then these Jews, whose souls were just about to depart from their bodies, were permitted to return to town. When they were well enough to stand on their own feet, they left Nachrovah in search of their brethren. They wandered from place to place until they ended up in Cracow, where they met Peretz and Yonah and the rest of the Jewish partisans, and told them their story. After Peretz heard the story of the ghetto Jews, he told them the story of the Jewish partisans.

Among the Jews who had come to Cracow and who listened to the stories of the ghetto Jews and the partisans were two men on whose left arms were tattooed blue numbers. The ghetto Jews and the partisans looked at the numbers questioningly. They had never before seen religious Jews with such tattoos. The two Jews told them, "We have come from Auschwitz." When the other Jews heard that, they were even more puzzled. What kind of answer was that? The two Jews with the tattoos then stood up and told their story.

They had been abducted from Nachrovah during one of the Germans' night excursions and had been sent to Auschwitz. Upon their arrival in Auschwitz, they met a population of thousands, almost all of them Jewish. Very few people died in Auschwitz. They were murdered before they had a chance to die. They were murdered very quietly. The voice which goes from one end of the world to the other when a soul leaves a body was not heard in Auschwitz. Hundreds of people were locked into a room. After a short time, when the door was opened, they were all found dead.

The dead were cremated in huge furnaces built especially for that purpose, and only their ashes remained.

This does not mean that everybody was murdered in the same way. In Auschwitz people were murdered by all kinds of cruel and terrible methods, but the gas chambers were the principal method.

The Jews listened to this story and lowered their eyes in pain and embarrassment — pain over what had happened to their martyred brothers, and embarrassment that they had told their own stories first. Compared to the story they heard from these two Jews, their own stories were like children's tales.

In Cracow, the Jews of Nachrovah found Jews who had been neither in Auschwitz, the ghetto, nor the forest. These Jews had been more fortunate. When the Germans and Russians divided up Poland between them, they found themselves living on the Russian side of the border. The Russians did not go so far as to put the Jews into a ghetto, but they did not trust them. They suspected the Jews of favoring the Germans, and so they exiled them all to Siberia. There, far away from the border, the Jews could not constitute a threat to Russia. The Jews from Siberia were unaware of what the Germans had done to their brothers in Nachrovah and Temyonovah. After the war, they were allowed to leave Siberia and to return to Poland, which had meanwhile been reunited in a pro-Russian Polish regime.

When the Auschwitz Jews heard the tales of the Jews from Siberia, they smiled and said, "We wish we had been with you. The cold of fear is much worse than the cold of snow." It was easier for the Jews in Russia to be afraid of dying from lack of food and lack of strength, than it was for the Jews in the ghetto to die of fear. You can only starve to death once, but you can die of fear many times.

On the other hand, when the Jews from Siberia heard the stories of the other Jews, they said, "We believe you, for we know you are honest, upright people and would not lie. Nevertheless, it's hard to accept what you have said. You must have exaggerated. Is it possible that such things as you have told really happened?" The other Jews tried, with little success, to prove to them that these things really had happened. The Siberian Jews listened patiently, but were not convinced. "Much of it is exaggerated," they said to themselves. It took a long time before they could really believe that there had been such a Holocaust.

The soil of Poland was soaked with Jewish blood; Jewish survivors could not remain there. The American Rescue Committee and the Jewish Agency transferred them to other countries — to France, Italy and, surprisingly, to Germany. Even though it was the Germans who had actually murdered the Jews, they had murdered more Jews in Poland than anywhere else in the world, thanks to Polish cooperation and encouragement.

When the State of Israel was proclaimed, the Jews from Auschwitz, the ghetto, the forest, and Siberia were finally permitted to immigrate to Israel. Those of them who had not already gone to America, now went to Israel. Every day a few more left. Those who didn't go immediately made their preparations. Preparations for *aliyah* are also a kind of *aliyah* because through these preparations their spirits rose even before their bodies made the actual physical *aliyah*. As time passed, almost everyone emigrated. A small group decided to remain in Poland and Germany, for reasons which remain beyond our comprehension.

When the immigrants arrived in Israel, they were housed in canvas tents and tin and wooden shacks and were given food. Quite some time would pass before they would receive permanent housing and jobs to support themselves. Houses must be built, and housing for all the Jews of Nachrovah could not be built in a day. Some of the immigrants complained, "After all we went through, the least we deserve is houses, not tents."

But Yonah told them, "Houses don't sprout up like mushrooms after the rain. They must be built, and that takes time. If you start today, you won't finish today. In a short time each one of us will have his own house, or at least a part of a house. Even in Nachrovah not everyone had his own home." When the Jews of Nachrovah heard what Yonah had to say, they realized he was right and stopped complaining.

Those Jews who were not working left their tents and shacks to explore the land and to see the Jewish state. The sight of signs hanging over storefronts printed in the holy tongue brought them back to life. In Nachrovah these letters had only been engraved on stone monuments for the dead; here they were engraved over the shops of the living. Passing a schoolyard, they saw crowds of children. When they listened to fragments of their conversation, they could understand very little. Yonah said, "From the little that I can grasp, I gather that they are speaking from their *siddurim* and *machzorim*. How nice that the children of Israel speak the language of the prayers of Israel." Each new thing they saw gave them cause to rejoice and forget their own problems.

Peretz also immigrated to Israel. He also toured the country, but he gave the dead precedence over the living — visiting them first. He went to Modiʻin where the Maccabees were buried. Then he went to Jerusalem, where the members of the Sanhedrin were buried. After that, he went to Tiberias and Safed where the sages of the Mishnah and Talmud and other outstanding, righteous Jews were buried. He stood with awe and admiration beside the caves where Israel's heroes and great men were buried. Everything that he had heard from the stories of Reb Naftali the Dayan came to life. Stories could not be seen or touched, but graves can be both seen and touched.

After he had fulfilled his duty to the dead, he went to visit the living. He visited Tel Aviv, Haifa and other places. He couldn't grasp much of what he saw. Many things were very different here than in Nachrovah or Temyonovah. He saw teenagers who looked just like their Polish counterparts in Temyonovah. When he heard them talking to each other in the holy tongue, he was astounded. When he was told that these boys were Jewish, he exclaimed, "How wonderful that in Eretz Yisrael even the *goyim* are Jewish!"

After Peretz had seen the country, he remembered Chaim. He had been Chaim's guardian since Shimon's death, and now it was his obligation to locate him and look after him. He had heard from the Jewish Agency representative in Cracow that Chaim was studying in a *yeshivah*. At that time there were not many *yeshivoth* in Eretz Yisrael so it was quite easy to find him. After trying one or two places, Peretz found Chaim.

Living together in canvas tents and wooden or tin shacks had united the Jews of Nachrovah physically and emotionally. When they finally received permanent housing, they separated, each one making his home in a different place.

In the beginning, they were so happy with their new houses that they thought of nothing else. But after a while, they began to miss the company of their *landsleit*. Nachrovah, the town they had known, no longer existed, but they couldn't forget it. It stood before their eyes even now, just as it had been before the Holocaust. They saw all the Jews of Nachrovah together in the synagogue. They saw all the Jewish houses and shops clustered around the market place, which was bustling on weekdays and quiet and peaceful on the Shabbath and holidays. They couldn't forget, nor did they want to. Living together, it had been easy to retain the feeling of Nachrovah. Each individual contributed his share, and the sum total of all their memories and recollections brought Nachrovah back to life.

Now that they had each gone their own way, they began to miss Nachrovah. Peretz had cursed Nachrovah and likened its fate to that of Sodom and Amorrah, but it was not the Jewish Nachrovah he had cursed; it was the Polish town, built upon the ruins of Jewish Nachrovah.

Peretz suggested, "Let us hold a convention of all the Jews from Nachrovah in Eretz Yisrael once a year. The sight of our *landsleit* will remind us again of Nachrovah." Peretz himself was from Temyonovah, but from the time that the Jews of the two cities were united in the forest, the towns themselves were considered as one.

The tenth of Teveth was chosen as the date for the convention of Jews from Nachrovah. This date had been designated by the Israeli Chief Rabbinate as the date upon which *Kaddish* would be recited for all Jews murdered by the Nazis. It would be appropriate for all the Jews of Nachrovah to recite *Kaddish* together for the martyred of their town.

Long after each meeting, memories of Jewish Nachrovah would remain before their eyes, as if the town were still there, and they would recall it lovingly. The Poles had succeeded in banishing the Jews from Nachrovah, but they could not succeed in banishing the memory of Nachrovah from its Jewish survivors. This annual meeting became an institution for the Jews from Nachrovah, held in a different place each year. It was their way of keeping the town alive.

But each year fewer and fewer people came to the convention on the tenth of Teveth. They did not forget their city, Heaven forbid. But each year the Angel of Death visited another few Jews whom the Nazis had not succeeded in wiping out. Their children, who were born in Israel, didn't attend the conventions. They had never seen Nachrovah and had no memories to relive.

One year a new member appeared. A gray-bearded Jew of about fifty entered, took a chair, and sat alone in the back of the hall. Observing him closely, it was obvious that he didn't understand what was being said, even though he was listening intently. Everyone was puzzled by this new guest. Usually Jews of one town do not attend the conventions of another. Was this Jew from Nachrovah? They glanced at him out of the corners of their eyes in order not to embarrass him, but no one could recognize him. They queried each other, but no one knew who he was.

There was something else which puzzled them. When they all rose to recite the *Kaddish*, he also rose. But he did not say a word. This was beyond comprehension. How could a Jew attending a memorial meeting listen to everyone recite *Kaddish* and not join in?

During the meeting, no one approached him. There was still the possibility that someone in the audience would identify their strange guest and inform the others. By the end of the meeting no one had. Finally, Yonah approached the guest. Before asking his name he gazed wonderingly into the man's face, which seemed familiar. The guest returned his gaze with a smile. Seeing that Yonah could not recall his name, the guest said in Polish, "Don't you remember me? I am from Nachrovah. My name is Ya'akov Shimeonovitz."

Yonah could not recall anyone in Nachrovah by that name. When the others saw Yonah talking to the guest, many of them approached, and stood in a circle surrounding them. Yonah turned to the circle and asked, "Do any of you know Ya'akov Shimeonovitz of Nachrovah?"

Someone asked, "What was his father's name?" The

guest answered with a smile, "My father was Shimon the *maskil.*" He pronounced the last word with a Yiddish accent.

His answer elicited shouts of surprise, "Mr. Shmendrikovitz, Mr. Shmendrikovitz!"

The guest said, "Don't call me Mr. Shmendrikovitz. Call me Ya'akov Shimeonovitz."

The circle did not disperse. Ya'akov Shimeonovitz stopped smiling. He rolled back his shirt sleeve and showed them the number tattooed on his left arm. Then he began to talk. Yes, he had been in Auschwitz. With his own eyes he had seen men, women and children brought into the gas chambers. With his own eyes he had seen them cremated afterwards. He had also seen people murdered in various other ways. In those days he had asked himself, "How could Christians, whose religion preaches mercy, do such cruel things?" Then he had examined his own heart. Realizing that he didn't believe in Jesus at all, he returned to Judaism. His own life had been saved miraculously, and he was one of the few who had survived the camps.

Ya'akov stopped talking and waited for questions. He knew that the Jews of Nachrovah had a great deal to ask him. When asked why he hadn't returned to Nachrovah, to his wife and daughter, after leaving Auschwitz, Ya'akov replied, "I did return to Nachrovah. When I entered my house, my wife and daughter weren't at home. Only Stashek, my brother-in-law, was there. When Stashek saw me he grabbed a knife and was about to kill me. I fled from the house and never returned. I know that Marussa will never return to me, nor will she give me Yanka. I wrote to her afterwards, while I was still in Poland, and I also wrote from here, but I have never received any response. She doesn't want to answer me." He paused and then added, "Or possibly Stashek never showed her my letters." He sighed and added again, "I made a great mistake in my life. Now I am left with nothing. I don't believe in Christianity, and I don't know anything about Judaism. I don't even know how to say *Kaddish*. I have lost both worlds."

The Jews of Nachrovah saw that Ya'akov Shimeonovitz had truly repented. They tried to forget the hard feelings they had held against him in their hearts all these years, and to replace them with a bit of love. Someone asked, "Mr. Shimeonovitz, why didn't you ever come to our meetings before?"

Ya'akov answered, "I never came before because I was embarrassed. Everyone wants to be seen at his best, not his worst. Do you know why I came today? I came because I had a dream. In my dream, my father appeared to me. He had a beard — not the short little beard that he had during his lifetime, but a long, Jewish beard — with a *tallith* around his shoulders and *tefillin* on his head.

"When he saw how amazed I was to see him with a long beard, *tallith*, and *tefillin* — things he never wore while he was alive — he smiled and said, 'Ya'akov, my son, I made a big mistake in my life. I thought Jews could live together with Christians. I didn't know the Christians. I made a mistake. You, who know them, flee from them if you want to live. Go to the Jews. Your place is with them.' When my father disappeared I opened my eyes and recalled the dream. That very day I read in the newspaper that the Jews of Nachrovah were holding a convention today, and so I overcame my embarrassment and attended. Now I feel better. I have fulfilled my father's wish."

When Ya'akov finished talking, the circle quietly dispersed. Ya'akov went home to his one-room flat with Peretz accompanying him. On the way, Peretz spoke to Ya'akov about Brachah and asked him if he would write one more letter to Marussa asking, incidentally, about Brachah. Perhaps this time Brachah's merits would guide the letter to Marussa's hands and help both of them. Ya'akov listened to Peretz and promised to fulfill his request, even though he himself had lost all hope of finding a way to Marussa's heart. Peretz gave Ya'akov his own address, said goodbye, and returned to his own home, which was also in Tel Aviv.

Ya'akov kept his promise. The very next day he sat down and wrote to Marussa, repeating everything that he had written in his previous letters. At the end of the letter he added a question about Brachah, the daughter of Yudel and Esther Glick. Did Marussa have any idea where she was today?

One afternoon, a month later, Ya'akov returned home from work and found a letter in his mailbox. Looking at the envelope, he recognized Marussa's handwriting. With trembling hands, he opened the envelope. In his excitement, his eyes were momentarily blurred, so that it took a few moments until he could read.

My dear Yank,

When I saw your handwriting, I almost fainted. I had always believed that you were no longer alive. When I recovered, I read and reread your letter, and even now I still cannot believe in my good fortune. This is the only letter I have ever received from you since your abduction from the ghetto of Nachrovah. The previous letters you spoke of never reached me. I miss you very much. I will do all I can to come to you in the Holy Land.

Yanka has written a few words at the end of my letter. Much has happened to us. My parents passed away a few years ago. Stashek is married and lives in the left wing of the house while Yanka and I live in the right. Three months ago Stashek and his wife went abroad to study and they have not yet returned.

With great longing and hopes to see you soon,

Marussa

P.S. Concerning Brachah, I can only tell you that her name was changed to Barbara Sokolsky, and she immigrated to the Holy Land about a year ago.

M.

Dear Father,

My happiness knows no bounds. I have been reborn. Now I have a father. I am studying and trying to be a good student. I will help Mother try to come to you soon, with all my might. Be strong and well and wait for us. We will surely come.

Your loving daughter,

Yanka

That very day, Ya'akov went to tell Peretz about the letter. Peretz read the lines about Brachah and was overcome with surprise and happiness. Early the next morning he traveled to Jerusalem to tell Chaim that his sister Brachah was in Israel.

Chaim was now learning in the famous *yeshivah*, Yeshivath haMathmidim. When Chaim heard Peretz's news, he closed his *gemara* and went with Peretz to the offices of the Jewish Agency. They wanted to look through the list of Polish immigrants and see exactly when Barbara Sokolsky had arrived in Israel and where she was now. But no such name appeared on the Jewish Agency list. Chaim was terribly disappointed. Peretz immediately returned to Tel Aviv to ask Ya'akov to write a second letter to Marussa, asking for the exact details of Barbara Sokolsky's immigration. Meanwhile Chaim returned to his study of *gemara*. His hope had been strengthened. Brachah was alive and in Eretz Yisrael, and with God's help, he would find her yet.

Why didn't Marussa write Yank that Barbara Sokolsky had not immigrated through the Jewish Agency, but rather in the service of the Catholic Church? Perhaps she didn't write about it because she too was a Catholic and didn't want to disturb the Catholic missionary activity. She was obligated to answer the question about Brachah truthfully, since Brachah had been entrusted to her care, but she was not obligated to reveal the secrets of the Catholic mission.

◄§ 25 §► *Marcus Feldsher*

There were four members in the Feldsher family: Marcus, his wife, Rosa, and their daughters, Sabina and Coralla. Marcus was a little over forty, and Rosa was a little under forty. Sabina was twelve and Coralla ten. They had only been in the country for a few months. The Jewish Agency had found them in one of the refugee camps in Germany and had put them on a boat to Israel.

Before the war, the Feldsher family had lived in Pihokovah, a small town with a small population, many of whom were Jews. The non-Jews were farmers, and the Jews were merchants or craftsmen. Marcus was a barber whose services were needed by all. Every Jew in Pihokovah had to have a haircut before the holiday, and some shaved their beards or had them trimmed every Friday in honor of the Sabbath. Non-Jews also needed a barber once in a while. Of course, Marcus couldn't get rich by being a barber. It is doubtful if he could even have supported himself at all had he not had a few other skills on the side. On Sundays and Wednesdays he dealt in medicine and bloodletting for a few important householders. He could have done this on Fridays too, but on Fridays, he was busy with haircuts and shaves and had no time for anything else.

And any Jew who was kept awake by a toothache during a long winter night, and who was reminded of the saying of our Sages, "Man would have been better off had he not been created," would rise with the first crow of the rooster, gather up his courage, and wake up Marcus to take care of his tooth. Marcus was not in favor of prolonged treatments. He would hide a tiny set of tongs in the sleeve of his white coat and would tell his patient to recite, "Open your mouth and let your teeth shine."

Marcus would then act quickly and the Jew would cry "Oy!" Before he could cry "Oy!" a second time, Marcus would smile and show him his tooth caught in the tongs, as if to say, "There is no more reason to cry 'Oy.'" Truth to tell, Marcus did not really deceive his customers. Everyone in town was aware of Marcus's method of treating toothache. Nevertheless, when the time came, everyone was willing to be deceived. Apparently it was easier that way. It took too much courage to look straight at the tongs. From all of these occupations, Marcus managed to eke out a respectable living.

He was not very stringent in his observance of the *mitzvoth*. As a matter of fact, he was as lenient as he could be. He had sinned by shaving off Jewish beards and had repeated this act so many times that other prohibitions also seemed permissible to him. But every Shabbath and holiday he came to the synagogue. There he had a seat among the important householders, and this in itself sufficed to draw him there. Compared to the pharmacist, Pan Isaak, Marcus was extremely religious. Pan Isaak attended synagogue only once a year, on Yom Kippur, while Marcus came every

Shabbath and holiday. Since he was more "Jewish" than the pharmacist, he was not called "Pan."

During the war, Marcus and his family suffered much. After the war, Marcus saw that many Jews were immigrating to Israel, and he thought, "What shall I do in a Poland without Jews? My whole livelihood depends on Jews. The Poles don't let blood or have toothaches. My place is among the Jews." He acted accordingly and immigrated together with the others to Eretz Yisrael.

Marcus received a two-room apartment and, after much effort, a store in the neighborhood shopping center to open a barbershop. At first he blessed the Jews and their state, but he was soon disillusioned. He couldn't make a living from his trade in his neighborhood. All the men worked outside of the neighborhood, and if they needed a shave or a haircut, they would get one near their place of work. Neither did the Jews in the neighborhood have time to let blood. Anyone who had a toothache would go into town to an expert dentist who would treat the tooth for several months before extracting it.

Greatly disappointed, Marcus went to the Jewish Agency office and complained to the clerks that he had been misled. Had he known what the situation was, he wouldn't have come. The clerks answered him, "You're not the only one with complaints. Many people are dissatisfied. Many have complained before you and surely many will complain in the future. Do what everyone else does."

Marcus asked, "And what does everyone else do?"

They answered, "A person who needs to support himself takes any work that he can find."

Marcus was insulted by this advice and thought to himself, "These clerks don't know me and don't know how important and respected I was in Pihokovah, or they would never speak to me like this." At first he was about to tell them who he was and what he had done in Pihokovah. Then he decided not to say anything. It was beneath his dignity. He had heard that others in the same position banged their fists on the clerks' desks, and if necessary even lifted a chair and threw it at the clerk's head, but he would not do such a thing. It was beneath his dignity. Marcus, his heart bitter, left the clerks and knew not where to turn.

We have no idea how the missionaries discovered that Marcus was so bitter, but it makes no difference. They found out and they sent an agent to him.

One day, someone knocked on Marcus's door. Marcus was sitting at home, pondering his sad plight. He called out in a loud voice, "*Ken*," one of the few Hebrew words he had learned from his daughters. The door opened and a tall thin man entered. Marcus looked at him and saw that he was not one of the neighbors. He knew them all already. Seeing that he was a stranger, Marcus motioned to a chair and invited his guest to sit down. The man thanked him and began to speak in a weak, thin, voice, counting his words as though they were pearls. Marcus strung the words together and gathered that the guest was asking if he, Marcus, would agree to accept help in his plight.

Marcus was insulted. To take help from others? Was he a beggar, Heaven forbid, to take help from others? Nevertheless, he showed no signs of being insulted nor did he insult his guest. He was depressed after his conversation with the clerks, and he restrained himself. First he would hear what the man had to say.

Marcus asked, "What do you wish to do for me?"

The guest answered, "If you are interested in emigrating to another country, we will help you."

When Marcus heard that, he felt differently. This was a very dignified offer. After all, even rich people who want to emigrate need help. Marcus asked, "Which country can you help me reach?"

The guest answered, "We can bring you to many countries."

Marcus asked, "For instance?"

The guest answered, "For instance, Brazil."

When Marcus heard that, he was ready to jump for joy, but he restrained himself. It was beneath his dignity. Just then, Marcus recalled that he had not asked his guest's name or whom he represented. Marcus said, "Excuse me, sir. Please tell me who you are, and what your name is."

The guest answered, "My name is Peter." Marcus looked at him, surprised. The man spoke Yiddish as well as any Jew, but he had never heard of any Jew with a name like Peter. Peter saw his surprise and said, "My name used to be Shimon, but after I came to the truth, I changed my name to Peter."

Marcus asked, "What truth do you mean?"

Peter answered, "I mean the truth of Christianity." Marcus began to ponder his words and didn't know what to say further. Peter said, "All that we ask of you is to accept our help. Jesus commanded us to help others, and we are fulfilling his command. We don't ask anything from you but to believe in Jesus. That belief is sufficient for us."

Marcus sat there, not knowing what to answer. On the one hand, the offer was incredible — to send him to Brazil. On the other hand, he was a Jew and didn't believe in Jesus. Although he was not strictly observant, he did believe in God. When Peter saw his bewilderment, he said, "You don't have to believe in Jesus wholeheartedly. You merely need a document stating that you have been baptized a Catholic. That's all you have to do."

After pondering this for a while, Marcus said, "I need time to think about this. Please come back in three days' time."

Peter rose, offered his hand to Marcus, smiled and said "Shalom." Marcus shook his hand weakly and Peter left. It must be noted that Marcus was not inclined to follow Peter, but he didn't have the courage to refuse his help.

When Rosa returned home shortly after, Marcus told her all that had happened. Rosa didn't think twice. "Thank God!" she said.

Marcus asked, "Why are you thanking God?"

Rosa replied, "I thank God for sending us an angel of mercy. I owe so much money to the grocer that I have no idea how to pay the debt." Marcus, seeing that his wife was in favor of accepting Peter's help, began to doubt himself. Perhaps Rosa was right?

That very evening Peter came by with a large package of food and clothing. Had he brought the package in the morning, Marcus would have thrown him out of the house. He was not a beggar. But now that they were discussing the possibility of emigration to Brazil, the matter of the package was of secondary importance. Peter would not sit down, as he was in a hurry. He didn't want to influence Marcus in any way. In matters like this one must be guided by one's own conscience.

Sabina and Coralla were home when Peter came. They saw the man and the package and heard what he said. They knew something had happened at home that they were unaware of, and their curiosity was aroused. Listening in on their parents' conversation after the man had gone, they realized that their parents were thinking of leaving Israel. This possibility saddened them. They had good teachers and close friends from whom they didn't want to part.

For three days and three nights doubt gnawed at Marcus's heart unmercifully, until it seemed to him that it would eat away a hole. Rosa's heart remained untouched. She tried to convince Marcus that what Peter was asking was not such a terrible thing. What difference did a piece of paper make? In his heart, he could remain the same as he had always been. Rosa's tongue was as soft as butter as she tried to help both her husband and Peter.

Nevertheless, when Peter returned three days later, Marcus answered neither yes or no. The three days had not been sufficient for him to reach a decision. Rosa, who had made sure she would be home then, began to answer yes. Marcus gave her a sharp look, and she refrained. She both respected and feared her husband, and he didn't allow her to dominate him.

This time, also, Peter had not come empty-handed. The package he brought only served to increase Marcus's agitation. Nevertheless, he could not bring himself to say yes.

When Peter saw that Marcus was not so easily convinced, he changed his tactics and said, "If you are not willing to accept the offer we made to you, perhaps we can help you in a different manner." When Marcus heard that his eyes lit up. What a relief that Peter had dropped the idea of baptism. Had he kept on discussing it, Marcus might have given in. Now he listened carefully to Peter's new proposal. Peter said, "We will accept your daughters in our school, tuition free. They will also eat there and receive proper clothing for free."

When Marcus heard this proposal, a great stone was lifted from his heart. He saw nothing wrong with this idea, and he could not refuse the good-hearted Peter another time.

Marcus quickly answered yes like one who is afraid of missing his chance. Rosa nodded her agreement and Peter smiled with satisfaction.

৵ 26 ৼ *The Mission School*

Marcus accompanied his daughters to their new school in Jerusalem. After Peter had gone that evening, he realized that he had acted hastily in agreeing so quickly but to change his mind now would be beneath his dignity. He could not hesitate and waver all the time. Nevertheless he wanted to see with his own eyes what the place was like.

They reached Jerusalem towards evening, as Peter had advised him. When they reached the Convent of St. Paul it was already dark outside. Marcus's heart was filled with impressions of his trip. This was the first time he had traveled to Jerusalem, and he was greatly affected by the Judean hills. They did not look like any other place that he had seen before in Eretz Yisrael. The other scenery in Eretz Yisrael resembled similar views all over the world, but these hills seemed to be shrouded in mystery. Wherever there is mystery, there is sanctity. As he rode in the bus, he looked out the window with awe.

At that time he thanked God that he had not succumbed to Peter's enticements and had not agreed to detach himself from the Jewish people. This sanctity of the Judean hills belonged to the Jewish people and to himself.

One who cut himself off from the Jews would have no part in the sanctity of these hills. Jewish heroes such as the Maccabees had fought for these hills. The *Beith haMikdash* had been in Jerusalem. As long as he remained Jewish he would always have a share in this. How stupid Peter was to have broken away from all of this. Marcus lost his respect for Peter and regretted that he had not refused the offer of the school, too. But now it was too late. He was already in Jerusalem and was obliged to enter the school and see for himself what kind of people would be educating his daughters. Now and then Marcus gazed at his daughters' eyes and saw their dejection. Probably they were depressed that he had taken them out of the Shivath Tzion school. Were they right? Was a Catholic mission school the proper place for Jewish girls?

Lost in his thoughts, Marcus found himself standing before the narrow gate of a large courtyard, his two daughters beside him. At this time of day, the gate was not locked so he opened it, and they entered. Deep inside stood a building. They approached it and stood before a heavy, locked door. Marcus rang the doorbell. The tall young man who opened the door asked whom they wished to see. Marcus quietly answered that Peter had told him to bring his two daughters here. When the man heard Peter's name he smiled thinly and invited them inside. Then he closed the door and led them along a long, dark hallway. When he knocked, someone inside answered, "Yes." The young man opened the door, showed Marcus and the girls inside, and closed the door after them.

Sitting at a massive desk inside the room was a middle-aged man, a huge cross hanging on his chest. When Marcus saw the cross he had an urge to run away, but felt it was beneath his dignity. The girls looked at each other in amazement.

Lucas, the head of the convent, offered Marcus a chair. Marcus hesitantly approached and sat down. The girls remained standing. Lucas asked, "What do you wish, good sir?"

Marcus answered, "Peter sent me here."

Lucas said, "Then you want to enroll your daughters in our school." Marcus nodded his head in agreement but did not say a word. Lucas pressed a button on the table, and in a few seconds the door opened and a dark haired girl of about twenty appeared at the door. Lucas gestured to her and she entered. Lucas, looking at the girl and pointing to Marcus, said, "This good man has brought you two new pupils." Barbara looked at the girls and smiled.

"Sit down, Barbara," said Lucas. Barbara took a seat opposite Marcus and gestured to the girls to sit down on the chairs along the wall.

Suddenly Barbara turned to Marcus and asked him in Yiddish what his name was. Marcus lost his wits. So far the conversation had been in Polish. That was understandable. These people were apparently Catholics from Poland. But what connection did Catholics have with Yiddish? The girls also looked at Barbara in astonishment. Marcus didn't answer her question. He was so taken aback by her Yiddish that he completely forgot that he had been asked a question. Barbara smiled warmly and repeated her query, which he now answered. She then asked, "Are you Jewish?"

This time Marcus nodded his head in affirmation. Barbara said, "I, too, am Jewish."

At this, Marcus breathed deeply and said "Yes?" in a questioning tone.

Barbara laughed and said, "What is so surprising? The first Christians were all Jewish. Even Jesus Christ was Jewish."

Actually, Barbara had not told him anything new, and he wondered that he had never before been aware of the close relationship between Jews and Christians until Barbara had spelled it out. They had always seemed to him to be worlds apart. Now Barbara had come and broken down the barrier separating them.

Then Barbara turned to the girls and asked them in Hebrew for their names, ages and grades in school. The girls answered the questions with no hesitation. Barbara's Hebrew attracted them to her very much. Sabina said that she was twelve and in sixth grade. Coralla said that she was ten and in fourth grade. Marcus wondered to himself whether they really spoke Hebrew in the convent. Barbara said, "If you agree to entrust me with the education of these lovely girls, I shall be delighted. And we will also teach them Hebrew."

Marcus was deeply touched by and appreciative of this lovely girl who was so anxious to teach his two daughters, tuition free. He could not speak, and his eyes filled with tears — not tears of sorrow, but tears of gratitude. Barbara said, "I see that you agree to entrust me with the girls and I am very happy. You can go home with a quiet heart. Your girls are in good hands."

Marcus arose, went over to the girls and kissed them, and then nodded to the man with the cross, thanking him in Polish. Finally he bowed to Barbara and thanked her in Yiddish, choosing this language to emphasize his warm feelings towards her and the confidence she had inspired in him. Barbara smiled at Marcus as if to say, "I understand you." She escorted him to the door, and he left the building.

All the way home from Jerusalem, Marcus was very happy. Barbara's image stood before him the whole way, never leaving him. "Such a fine young Jewish woman! There are few like her," thought Marcus. "There can be no danger in entrusting the education of my daughters to a girl like that." He was so deeply absorbed by these thoughts that he forgot to look out the window at the Judean hills. Soon the trip was over and he was home.

But Marcus did not sleep peacefully that night. As a matter of fact, he hardly slept at all. After he told Rosa all that had happened to him in Jerusalem, repeating everything that he had seen and heard there, the scenes repeated themselves in his dreams and disturbed his sleep. Rosa, on the other hand, was extremely happy and accused her husband of not having trusted Peter. She had had faith in him from the very beginning. The plan to go to Brazil was also a very good one. Marcus answered, "Even if Brazil was a good idea, I have no intention of taking the girls out of their new school, so there is no point in discussing any trip now."

Sabina and Coralla received clean beds for the night and fine new clothes for the day, and they were happy. Nevertheless, they also had a few unpleasant surprises. There were forty girls in the school, thirty of them Jewish. Before bedtime, all the girls knelt down before an icon of the mother and child in the corner of the room and recited prayers. Sabina and Coralla were angry and upset. They knew that Jews do not kneel during prayers nor do they stand in front of any picture while praying. In the Shivath Tzion school they had studied the Torah which commands, "You shall not make for yourself any statue or picture." In their bewilderment they looked to Barbara who herself was kneeling with the other girls. They saw that she was smiling at them, and they were reassured. If Barbara agreed to such practice, perhaps there was no harm in it.

On Shabbath there were no special prayers. It was just like every other day of the week. On Sunday a festive prayer service was held. The girls all kneeled for a long time, singing hymns. Whenever Sabina and Coralla saw strange things in their new school and were not sure how to behave, they turned to Barbara. She was Jewish so she would tell them if it was right for them or not. They did not ask her with words, but with their eyes. She answered them in the same way, not with her mouth, but with her eyes. Barbara's warm smile sanctioned the practices of the convent, and her approval allayed their anxiety. The girls trusted her completely because she was Jewish. She knew better than they did what actions befitted Jewish girls.

Of course Sabina and Coralla were homesick for their parents and their friends from the Shivath Tzion school. Once, they appealed to Barbara, and she promised to allow them to go home for a visit when the time came. The girls didn't know when this would be, but they rejoiced in the promise. They saw that none of the other girls went home and realized that that was the rule of this school. The fact that they were no exception comforted them.

◄§ 27 §► *Marussa Comes to Israel*

Marussa and Yanka were planning to immigrate to Israel, to be with Yank. Marussa was in a great hurry. She had to leave the house before Stashek returned home. She had no doubt that if Stashek were home he would do everything in his power to prevent her from going to Israel. She didn't hold it against him. She could actually even sympathize with him. This move would stain their family name with a stain which could never be erased. It was no small thing for a Polish Catholic woman to be the wife of a Jew and live in a Jewish state. Nevertheless she was not willing to abandon Yank. She knew that this was also the best thing for her daughter, Yanka. More than once Yanka had been insulted by her Polish schoolmates, who called her "Jidovka" — dirty Jew.

Even in post-war Poland, under a pro-Russian regime, Jews were not loved. Marussa didn't know whose fault this was, but she knew it was a fact. She had been told that even in Russia itself there was anti-Semitism. This was a bit hard for her to believe. She had always heard the Poles accusing the Jews of being Communists. If so, the Communists should like the Jews. But she was no expert in politics, and all the explanations that she had heard about anti-Semitism made no sense to her.

In actuality, it made no difference to her whether the anti-Semites were right or not. All that mattered to her was that the Jews were hated everywhere, and that her daughter was considered a Jew. She was not willing for Yanka to be at the mercy of other people's hate. Until now she had been powerless to help Yanka and had tried to ignore her troubles, but now that Yank was alive and living in the Jewish state, she must take Yanka there as well. Then she would never again have to hear anyone call her "Jidovka."

Yank's latest letter inspired Marussa to work even harder to leave Poland. He described the country as being very beautiful. He wrote of the tall buildings being erected, the public parks and lovely wide boulevards in the larger towns; the *kibbutzim* and *moshavim* whose members worked with great enthusiasm.

Marussa assumed that Yank had exaggerated greatly. She wasn't foolish enough to believe every word of the letter. After all, no one can change his skin, and she had known Jews for a long time. She couldn't believe that Jews could build houses with their own hands. She had never even seen a Jew on a scaffold. The business about Jews on *kibbutzim* and *moshavim* was also not clear to her. A Jew working in the field? A Jew milking a cow? A Jew raising chickens? None of these was work for a Jew. Least of all could she believe in the parks. She laughed at the picture of a Jew holding a flower. Yank had just written these things to heighten her desire to join him. Nevertheless, he couldn't be making it all up. He was certainly exaggerating, but there must be a grain of truth in it. Even one grain of truth made her very curious to see it all with her own eyes.

Yanka also encouraged her mother to act. In her first letter she had promised her father that she would do so, and she kept her promise. She, too, could not ignore the name "Jidovka" which she was called from time to time. True, it did not affect her as strongly as it did her mother. She told herself that it was true and nothing to be ashamed of. Nevertheless, she was hurt because she knew that those who called her names intended to insult her.

When Marussa reached Yank's question about Brachah at the end of his letter, she was disconcerted. Was it her duty to write that Barbara had gone to the Holy Land in the service of the mission, and not with the Jews? After all, she herself was a Catholic. How could she reveal matters which the Church wanted kept secret? At first she thought that she would simply ignore the question. It would look as if she had just forgotten to answer one part of the letter. Later she decided to give an unclear answer. She would write that since she was to immigrate to Israel as quickly as possible, there was no need to answer this question in writing. She would tell him everything she knew about Barbara Sokolsky once she arrived in Israel. Whoever was waiting for Barbara had already waited a long time and could wait a little bit longer. Once she had seen Yank in person she would decide whether she should tell him the whole story or withhold part of it. She would know then who was waiting for Barbara and whether there was any danger to Barbara in revealing all that she, Marussa, knew about her. For now, she would keep her secret.

Marussa had already visited the capital several times in order to speed up the arrangements for her journey. Each time she made the trip she did so secretly because she was afraid that if her neighbors ever found out, they would not hesitate to ridicule and scorn her. To them, immigration to the Jewish state was equivalent to becoming Jewish. They would consider her a heretic. She also feared that if her travel plans became known, Stashek would find out and return home to prevent her passage. No one must find out until she had left Nachrovah.

Unfortunately, all her precautions were to no avail. It can only be guessed how her secret was exposed. One possibility is that the postman suspected something. Marussa — like many other people — received letters from abroad from time to time. As long as the letters came infrequently, they aroused no curiosity; but when they began to arrive regularly, the postman began to wonder. What connection did Marussa, whose parents and grandparents had been born in Nachrovah, have abroad? The postman searched for a return address on the envelope, but found none. This seemed quite strange to him, for it was customary to write the name and address of the sender on the back of the envelope so that in case the letter could not be delivered, it could be returned.

Next, the postman examined the writing on the stamp but did not recognize its large strange letters. He looked more closely and found small print in Latin letters below the stamp. These letters formed the word Israel. The postman knew that Israel was the Jewish state, and he wondered what connection Polish Marussa had with Jewish Israel.

When he returned home from work, he discussed this with his neighbors, and they discussed it with their friends until all Nachrovah assumed that Marussa was about to go to

Israel. Whom could she have in Israel? That they didn't know. As far as they knew, Yank Shmendrikovitz had been murdered together with all the other Jews of the ghetto. It must be one of Yank's relatives who was writing to her. Although no one knew what was written in the letters, they guessed that she wanted to go to Israel. Had she been a good Catholic, she would never have corresponded with a Jew. If she was writing to them, her heart must be with them. Yank had poisoned her heart, and she couldn't free herself from Jewish sorcery. True, she had brought Barbara to the convent and had been present at her baptism, but that was only for the sake of keeping up appearances. In her heart she was Jewish, and as such, she was a traitor.

No one approached Marussa, but she read in their eyes their knowledge of her secret. She read both scorn and hatred, and she knew she must leave Nachrovah as quickly as possible. Every additional day that she remained endangered her journey. It was even possible that someone had already notified Stashek, or had set some other pitfall for her. The sooner she left, the better.

Marussa traveled to the capital once more. From there she sent her last letter to Yank, asking him not to write any more to Nachrovah, for her secret had been exposed and his letters might even be opened. If it were known who was writing and exactly what her plans were, it could harm her. Aside from that, there was no need for him to write any more, for the passport agency had promised that she could leave Poland in two months on a plane to Rome, and from there she would make her way to Israel.

Marussa returned to Nachrovah with mixed feelings of

happiness and fear—happiness that she now knew the date of her departure and fear that something would happen at the last minute—or that Stashek would return just before she had left.

Marussa was not in an enviable position in those days. The number of days seemed endless. Each one was fifty years long. The nights were no better. Various strange dreams—both good and bad—disturbed her sleep, and from time to time she would wake up, excited, her heart beating fast.

Sometimes, in her dreams, she would see herself walking down the sun-drenched streets of Israel, Yank on one side of her, Yanka on the other. Yank would be telling her all he had gone through during the years they had been separated and she would be listening and sighing. She would be sighing, not from grief, but from relief that it was all over and had ended happily.

In another dream, she saw Stashek, his face ablaze, run to the kitchen and grab a long knife to murder her for wanting to go to the Jewish state. Suddenly Yank was standing beside her, and she was afraid that Stashek would murder Yank. In her terror she began to scream. At that moment she felt a caress. A soft hand touched her gently. When Marussa opened her eyes she saw her daughter's hand, as Yanka said, "Mother, you must have had a bad dream."

When the day of departure arrived, there was no one happier than Marussa. Had the wait been any longer, she might not have endured.

Sabina and Coralla had not returned home for over two months, although the girls had written several times that they would come, and Rosa missed them. Rosa began to be angry with the convent staff for not permitting her daughters even a short visit home. "Don't they understand a mother's heart?" she asked herself. Nevertheless, she didn't discuss her feelings with Marcus. She didn't want to give him any reason to find fault with Peter, as she had not yet given up her hope that he would sent them to Brazil. Although she would not allow herself to express her anger at the mission staff, she still could tell Marcus how much she missed her daughters. One day, Rosa suggested, "Shouldn't we go to Jerusalem to visit our girls?"

"Yes," Marcus answered, "Let's go."

"When?" asked Rosa.

"Tomorrow," answered Marcus. "I have no work today and will have none tomorrow. At least I have plenty of time to travel."

Rosa comforted him, "Don't be discouraged, Marcus. You will have work yet. Peter is a good man and he won't forget us."

The next day Marcus and Rosa set out for Jerusalem. They left early in the morning in order to return home that same day. Last time Marcus had returned home late at night and had just managed to catch the last bus from Jerusalem to Tel Aviv; had he been any later he would have had to stay in Jerusalem overnight. This time they would have to be more careful. They didn't know anyone in Jerusalem, and they surely couldn't afford a hotel.

The sun climbed over the Judean hills, playing a game of light and shade. Rosa looked at the hills but saw nothing special. Marcus, also looking at the scenery, wondered why these hills made no impression on him now, when the first time he had not been able to take his eyes off them. Was it because he had already seen them once before? Perhaps. But it seemed to him that it also had to do with the convent. Since he had enrolled his daughters in the mission, these hills had lost their beauty for him. Now he recalled that he hadn't noticed the scenery on his way home from the convent either even though he had been sitting by the window the whole time. If one is not interested, he can look at something a million times, but not really see it even once.

Marcus and Rosa arrived in Jerusalem and transferred from the Egged bus to a Hamekasher bus which brought them to Inquisition Street. St. Paul's Convent was No. 6. As they approached the courtyard gate, the guard recognized Marcus and let them in. Sabina and Coralla were playing with the other girls. They were so absorbed in their game that they didn't notice their parents' entry.

Two young women came up to Marcus and Rosa and welcomed them. Marcus immediately recognized Barbara, the Jewess, and gave her a friendly smile. Barbara introduced them to Paulina, who was Sabina and Coralla's teacher. Paulina said, in a German that was similar to Yiddish, "You have lovely daughters."

Barbara added, "I also like them," and she smiled.

Rosa blushed, saying, "Lovely girls have lovely teachers."

Just then, Sabina and Coralla came running up and fell into their parents' arms with cries of joy. When they finally let go of their parents, Barbara told them something and they answered her gracefully. Marcus and Rosa listened, amazed. They knew that their daughters spoke Polish, Yiddish and Hebrew. Now they had spoken another language. When Rosa inquired, Barbara informed her that they were speaking French.

Marcus and Rosa asked simultaneously, an amazed expression on their faces, "French?"

Barbara said, "The girls have begun to learn French. We also teach foreign languages here." That was enough to make Rosa forgive the mission people for not letting the girls come home for a visit. Marcus licked his lips with his tongue and repeated the magic word, "French," in a whisper. Barbara didn't forget to add a few words in Yiddish. Although Rosa had already heard from her husband that there was a Jewish teacher in the convent who spoke Yiddish just like a Jew, now that she had heard her with her own ears, she could not help but be impressed. Barbara saw the impression she had made on Rosa with her Yiddish and realized her great power.

Barbara invited the guests into the house so that they

could rest up a bit from their trip and spend some time with their daughters. As they walked down the corridor, Lucas — a large gold cross on his chest — passed by and greeted them. Marcus returned his greeting with his head bowed, but Rosa did not answer him. Although she had known that this was a Jesuit convent, the actual sight of the cross confused and overwhelmed her. After Lucas had passed them, she regained control of herself and was ashamed of her behavior.

Marcus and Rosa spent two pleasant hours in the convent, their hearts happy and relieved. Everything was clean and neat. Everything here was respectable. People were generous and polite, wanting only to help them. The cross that Lucas, the chief clergyman, wore was a bit repugnant, but on the other hand, Barbara was Jewish and even spoke Yiddish. Before Marcus and Rosa left the convent, they went over to Barbara and asked her to allow the girls to come home for a visit once in a while. Barbara listened to their request and said, in Yiddish, "I have already promised them this more than once. Had you not come today, they would have gone to visit you tomorrow." Had anyone else said that to them, they probably would not have believed him, but because Barbara was a Jewish girl who only wanted to help them they believed her.

Sabina and Coralla walked with their parents to the courtyard gate and stopped there. Rosa tried to persuade them to accompany her and their father to the bus stop, but the girls shook their heads. When Marcus asked them why not, the girls said that they had already requested permission but Barbara would not allow it. Rosa was a bit surprised at this refusal, but she did not want to doubt Barbara's intentions. Perhaps it was not under Barbara's control. Rosa and Marcus took leave of their daughters with warm kisses and promises to come again to visit.

Marcus and Rosa had to stand in line to wait for the bus home. As the line got longer and longer, and the bus still didn't come, Marcus impatiently turned around to check the length of the line and express his bitterness over the bus's delay. His glance fell on a young man who happened to be standing just behind him in the line. Marcus was astounded. The young man was Chaim. Had it been a girl, Marcus would have cried, "Barbara!" but it was a boy who stood next to him, not a girl. It is not polite to stare at strangers, so Marcus looked away from Chaim. But he couldn't contain himself for long and he soon turned his head to glance at Chaim again. He tried to appear preoccupied so that the boy wouldn't notice his staring. His amazement grew greater and greater. Never in his life had he seen two people who resembled each other so much.

Marcus whispered to Rosa who was standing in front of him. A few seconds later, Rosa turned her head and looked, as if unintentionally, at the boy standing behind her husband. Marcus had used all his will power to keep himself from staring at the boy, but Rosa could not contain herself. Her curiosity was much too strong, and she turned her head a second time and stared at the boy until he was embarrassed.

Chaim realized that the couple in front of him were staring at him with great interest, and he wondered what they saw in him to make them stare so. He looked just like thousands of other young men his age. The bus finally arrived, and the people in front of Marcus and Rosa began to push forward. Marcus and Rosa, absorbed in looking at Chaim, didn't even notice the bus. They just moved forward automatically. As they drew nearer to the door of the bus, they began to turn their heads back and forth. They wanted to see when it was their turn to get on the bus, but they also wanted to look at Chaim as long as they could. Perhaps the boy would not be able to get on the bus.

Chaim wanted to ask them why they kept staring at him, but he was too shy. But finally he gathered up his courage and asked them what they were staring at. Marcus was taken aback by the question and didn't answer immediately. He hesitated and then said, "Today we saw a girl who looks just like you. You are as alike as two drops of water."

Chaim caught his breath and asked, his voice shaking, "Where did you see her?"

Marcus answered, "We saw her on Inquisition Street."

Chaim asked, "What's her name?"

Just then Rosa and Marcus reached the door of the bus and got on. Chaim also tried to get on, but the driver closed the door and he was left standing on the platform. His disappointment was unbearable. His heart cried out within him, and he began to pound the door of the bus, hoping the driver would open it and allow him to get on. But the bus began to move away.

In a little while, another bus arrived and Chaim got on. When he had calmed down a bit he recalled that the man had said that he had seen the girl on Inquisition Street. In his mind's eye, Chaim reviewed all the houses on that street until he reached the Jesuit convent. By this time, he already knew all of Jerusalem — all its streets, and all its houses. "Yes, on that street there is a convent." His heart began to beat fast. A convent. Who knows. Could it be Brachah? Could Brachah be in a convent? He became very excited. All the way to Tel Aviv he could not relax.

When he arrived at Peretz's house, Peretz came out to meet him sorrowfully. Peretz said, "A letter came from Marussa saying that she will arrive in Israel soon and then she will tell Yank all she knows about Barbara Sokolsky." Chaim told Peretz about the incident in the bus station in Jerusalem, and Peretz was infected by his excitement. "We must search for Brachah in Jerusalem," he said.

◄§ 29 §► *The Search Ends*

Eretz Yisrael was in an uproar. The mission had succeeded in infiltrating into many Jewish homes. The daily newspapers were full of accounts of the deeds of Peter and his friends. Many Jews had already left the country with their help, and many Jewish children had been lured into mission schools, where they were converted to Christianity and taught to hate those Jews who did not believe in Jesus. The newspapers asked, "Would Jews in a Gentile country dare to open missions and proselytize among the Gentiles?"

Both religious and non-religious Jews shared in the widespread sentiment of anger at the missionary activity. What was particularly disconcerting was the fact that the missionaries' methods were so deceitful and unscrupulous. They did not try to prove the truth of their beliefs in open discussion, but rather took advantage of the distress of the weak and poverty-stricken. A man who is starving for a loaf of bread and sees a package of food cannot judge impartially between truth and falsehood. A man who has found no gold in Eretz Yisrael may be blinded by the promise of gold abroad and he may not realize that he is being deceived.

The furor in the *yeshivoth* was even greater. These boys,

who were devoting all their time and strength to the study of Torah, could not forget that they had accepted upon themselves at Mount Sinai that dictum that, "All Jews are responsible for one another." They were not interested in proselytizing among the Gentiles, for whom observance of the seven *mitzvoth* of *bnei Noach* was sufficient, but they felt deeply the loss of each and every Jewish soul. Here there could be no compromise. The *yeshivah* boys couldn't hide their anger at the government which took no legal action to restrain the missionaries.

The students of Yeshivath haMathmidim were among the best in the country. They were also the leaders and the most active in the campaign to return Jews to their heritage. The students of this *yeshivah* were not content to simply express feelings of anger at the missions and at the inactivity of the government. One evening, they called a mass assembly of *yeshivah* students from all over the country to discuss missionary activity. They intended to develop a campaign to fight the missionaries, whose honey-coated tongues dripped lies and deceit.

Chaim came to the assembly. Each time he heard the word "mission," he felt as though someone had stabbed his flesh with a dagger. After the incident the day before in the bus station, Brachah had not left his thoughts. He pictured her with a cross hanging about her neck. As he put together all the details he had gathered about her, his conviction that Brachah was caught in the net of the mission became stronger and stronger. She had been in non-Jewish hands in Nachrovah. Her name had been changed to a Polish name, Barbara Sokolsky. She had immigrated to Eretz Yisrael, but not through the Jewish Agency. The man whom he had met at the bus station had seen her on Inquisition Street, where there was a Jesuit convent. Didn't all these details speak for themselves?

Those present at the assembly made many suggestions. Some said that Jews must be warned not to fall into the trap that the mission people had set for them. Some said that those unfortunate people must be helped, so that they would need no help from the mission. Some said that the government should be pressured to enact laws prohibiting devious missionary activity.

When it was Chaim's turn to speak, he rose and said, "Everything that you have suggested is helpful. All these things must be done. Jews must be warned of the danger of the missions. Unfortunate people must be helped before they fall into the hands of our enemies. Laws must be enacted prohibiting missionary activity. But all these things will take time. Meanwhile the danger is very grave. Every day more Jewish souls are lost. Something must be done immediately."

All eyes were glued to Chaim as he talked, all ears bent to catch his words. Chaim was held in great esteem. He was one of the outstanding students of the *yeshivah*, and his opinions were well thought out. When he paused for a minute, his friend David asked, "What do you suggest we do?"

Chaim answered, "We must make our way into the convents which have been barred to us and try to rescue the Jewish children who have been lured inside. Even if we don't succeed in getting them out — even if the mission staff and the police are able to prevent this — the publicity that this act will draw will awaken people to the danger and bring others to our side. It will also frighten the missionaries and cause them to limit their activities."

The words flowed from Chaim's mouth as if they had a will of their own. They expressed his determination and desperation to save his sister. Chaim had no time to wait for laws to be passed forbidding missionary activity. Brachah was in need of help now. She was in greater danger every day and must be saved as quickly as possible. When Chaim was asked which convent to enter, since it was impossible to enter them all, he answered, "We must begin with the convent on Inquisition Street in the holy city of Jerusalem." None of his friends questioned his choice, as any convent could have been chosen. So they agreed both to his proposal to hold an anti-missionary demonstration inside a convent, and to his choice of the Convent of St. Paul, on Inquisition Street.

The time for the demonstration was set for three o'clock the following afternoon. At that time, about a hundred eighteen- to twenty-year-old boys came to Inquisition Street. They came in small groups, each one from a different direction, in order not to arouse suspicion. When they were all on Inquisition Street, two boys went up to the gate and knocked. The guard came to the gate, peered through the peephole, and opened the gate a crack. When he asked what they wanted, they answered something or other, trying to engage him in a conversation. The guard was not happy with this conversation and tried to close the gate, but one of the boys put his foot in the opening. Just then, the

212 / The Twins

second boy gestured to the others, and all the boys, who had
been standing along the wall separating the convent yard
from the street, hurriedly pushed through the gate and into
the courtyard. The guard was pushed aside, dumbfounded.

The noise of all the footsteps and shouts of the
demonstrators brought all the priests and nuns out of the
convent, rushing outside to see what had happened. The
pupils of the mission school ran after their teachers. The
teachers, overwhelmed by all the excitement, completely
forgot to send their pupils back inside. When the demonstrators saw the mission staff, they began to shout slogans
such as: "Remove your hands from Jewish children!"; "No
more selling of souls"; and "Where were Christian charity
and mercy in the days of the gas chambers?" The mission
staff was struck dumb and made no attempt to chase the
demonstrators from their premises. They knew that the
demonstrators outnumbered them by far and that they were
no match for them. Lucas rushed inside to call the police.

Chaim feverishly searched among the nuns who had
come out to the yard. Then his eyes fell upon Brachah, and
he shouted with all his strength, "Brachah!" Chaim's friends
couldn't hear what he was shouting, because they were busy
shouting themselves, but Brachah heard Chaim's cry. When
she heard her Jewish name pronounced by one of the
demonstrators, her whole body shook. She turned towards
the voice and when her eyes met Chaim's, she fainted.

A tumult arose among the convent staff. From all sides,
the word resounded, "Water, water, water." Chaim tried to
push his way through to the place where Brachah had been
standing a minute before, but he was unsuccessful. The

mission staff surrounded Brachah, who lay on the ground, trying to revive her. Just then the police arrived and began to forcibly remove the demonstrators. This was no easy task. The boys held out as long as they could and refused to leave. Meanwhile, the priests brought the children and Barbara into the convent. When Chaim saw that the yard was empty, he stopped resisting the police efforts to drag him away. The tense encounter had left him thoroughly exhausted.

A few of the demonstrators, including Chaim, were held for questioning by the police. On the way to the police station, Chaim debated as to whether he should reveal his secret to the police or not. At last he decided not to say anything. It would be better if this did not get into the newspapers. If it were printed, the mission staff would find out also. They would certainly hide Brachah or send her away, and he would lose her. If they had no knowledge of his secret, he would find a way to meet Brachah and get her out. And his reasoning was indeed correct.

The next day, the papers printed that the demonstrators had hit one of the nuns and knocked her to the ground. This enraged many people. "Jews don't behave like that," they said. The priests had misled the newspapers. This was the story that they had told the investigators. The demonstrators denied it completely, but not everyone believed them. "There must be some truth to the story," said many. "If she wasn't beaten, why did she fall to the ground in a faint?" Chaim, his eyes burning, devoured every word that was printed about Brachah to find out if she was well. When he read in the papers that there was no cause for concern, he was relieved and began to plan his next step.

Two days later, Chaim took a walk by himself down Inquisition Street. He walked back and forth in front of building No. 6. He knew that Brachah had fainted because she had seen him, and now that she had seen him, she would realize that he would come back to meet her again. He was not mistaken. In a short time Chaim caught sight of her at the convent gate, signaling to him to lead her in the direction he wanted her to take. Chaim turned and began to walk towards Yaffo Road. Brachah left the convent yard, following a few paces behind, and holding a small package in her hand. Since they were so careful, we didn't want to disturb them, and we did not follow them any further than our eyes could reach. They soon disappeared from sight.

Barbara Sokolsky's disappearance from the convent worried the mission staff considerably. Either she had been kidnapped or she had run away. They knew that the demonstrators had not hit her. She had fainted, apparently from excitement. Being Jewish, perhaps she regretted the missionary work she had performed. If she had run away, it would not be in the best interests of the mission to publicize it. So after much debate, they decided not to inform the police of Barbara's disappearance.

It was a beautiful summer morning. The sun was high in the sky, and the streets of Tel Aviv were drenched in sunlight. Three women walked slowly down Sanhedrin Street, one young woman on either side of an older woman. The woman in the middle had her head covered, while the girls were bare-headed. As they passed us, we recognized them immediately. They were Marussa, Yanka, and Brachah.

This was the day when Marussa and Yanka had been summoned to the rabbinic court, to convert. For a year they had been trying to join the Jewish people through conversion, but the court was in no hurry to grant their request. They were told that it was not easy to be Jewish. A Jew is obligated to fulfill 613 *mitzvoth* plus all the rabbinic edicts protecting these *mitzvoth*. But they did not give in. If women who were born Jewish could bear this heavy responsibility, so could they, they told the court. Meanwhile, a year had passed until their case finally came before the court and was decided in their favor. During that whole year Marussa and Yanka had studied Jewish law and prepared themselves for the conversion.

The conversion ceremony was to take place today, and

Brachah accompanied them. After the conversion, Marussa's new name would be Ruth, and Yanka would be called Na'amah.

When they·entered the rabbinic court, we retraced our footsteps and went to visit Ya'akov Shimeonovitz. His house wore a holiday atmosphere. On a table in the center of the room was a gleaming white tablecloth covered with cakes and liquor. Around the table sat Ya'akov, the head of the house; Peretz and Yonah; Chaim and David; and Leah, Yonah's wife. They had taken a day off from work to be with Ya'akov Shimeonovitz on this, his day of rejoicing. They spoke not about current events but about things that had happened ten years earlier. They revived old memories. Those who were sitting here today lived more in the past than in the present. It was not the first time that they were telling these stories; nevertheless each time the stories seemed new to them.

Time flew by, and before they finished retelling one-thousandth of their tales, the door opened. Ruth, Na'amah, and Brachah entered. Those in the room stood up in their honor. There was a minute of deep silence. All the faces were serious, and all eyes were blurred.

Some tears were of happiness and some of grief. David's tears were of grief. From the moment that Brachah had returned to her brother, Chaim, he could not forget his sister, Sarah, who had been together with Brachah in the convent in Poland. But Sarah had remained in Poland. Brachah and Marussa told him that she had also been baptized, and no one knew where she was today. Even if she had immigrated to Eretz Yisrael with the mission, as Brachah had done, he didn't know how to find her. Sarah didn't resemble him as Brachah resembled Chaim, so he could not recognize her at first sight. It was a miracle that Chaim and Brachah were as alike as two drops of water. The tears of joy soon disappeared, but it took all of David's strength to hold his tears back. He didn't want to spoil the happiness of those assembled in the house today.

After a minute of silence, calls of "*mazal tov*" were heard from all sides. Everyone sat down, except for Ya'akov who poured liquor for everyone. Then he also sat down. Everyone took a sip and good wishes began to fly like angels around the room. Ruth and Na'amah were the most excited, for they had cut themselves off from one world and entered another. It was as if they had been born anew. To be reborn at the age of forty, or even at the age of twenty, is no light matter. But it had been impossible to live in two worlds at once — two worlds that could not coexist. And so they were relieved and joyful at having chosen to become Jews.

The guests spoke about everything except Brachah's escape from the mission in Jerusalem and Marussa and Yanka's conversion in Tel Aviv. They were all familiar with the Talmudic adage which prohibits a Jew from making derogatory remarks about Gentiles in front of a convert or his descendants unto the tenth generation. Therefore they avoided any subject which might bring them to disparage the Christians.

David sat absorbed in his own thoughts. Everyone knew what he was thinking. Ruth said, "Don't despair, David. Your fiancée, Brachah, and I are trying to find your sister. We have already begun our search and we are waiting for results." David thanked Ruth, but in his heart he believed that her words had no substance. Ruth had cut herself off from all her family in Nachrovah. She could never succeed in renewing her contacts with the Catholics of Nachrovah to the point that they would be ready to help her search for Silvana. Brachah would not succeed either. The newspapers in Israel had printed the story of Chaim and Brachah, and the story had undoubtedly reached Poland.

David was partially comforted by the fact that he was not alone in his troubles. As our Sages have said, *"Tzarath rabim chatzi nechamah"* — when trouble is shared by many, that in itself provides partial comfort. His sister, Sarah, was not the only lost Jewish soul. Rivkah, Rachel, Leah and Chavah had remained in Poland as Catholics. They were the ones he had heard about, but it was common knowledge that thousands whose names were not even known had assimilated, and they shared the plight of his sister.

After a while, the guests rose and took leave of their hosts. They all wished Ya'akov, his wife, Ruth, and their daughter, Na'amah, a long, happy life together. The hosts accompanied their guests to the gate, wishing them all the best and thanking them for rejoicing with them. On the street, the group split into couples: Peretz and his wife, Leah; Yonah and Chaim; David and Brachah.

When David and Brachah were alone, Brachah said, "What Marussa said about an attempt to locate Sarah is the truth. I also think that there is no cause for despair." David realized from Brachah's tone of voice that she was not saying this just to make him feel better. She spoke honestly and openly, with real hope and not just from wishful thinking.

Perhaps Brachah had some plan. After all, she was now personally involved. Sarah would soon be her sister-in-law. Nevertheless, David didn't ask Brachah exactly what she was planning to do to save Sarah. If she hadn't volunteered this information, he didn't want to cross-examine her or force her to reveal her plans. But a glimmer of hope was kindled in David's heart. He had heard tales of the deeds of Brachah's father and her mother, and he knew that they had been people of exceptional dedication. Brachah was their daughter. She might very well be like her parents. And with dedication, even the impossible can be accomplished.

We also share David's estimation of Brachah. She put her heart and soul into all that she did. When she was put into the convent in Nachrovah, she fought with all her heart and soul to preserve her Jewishness. Finally, when she was caught in the snares of the mission, she worked for them with great dedication. Now that she had been rescued and had returned to her people, she would certainly do everything in her power to save others. We believe that she will be able to accomplish the impossible. And if she is successful in her plan to rescue Sarah, we will spare neither time nor trouble to tell you that story too.

GLOSSARY

BAR MITZVA: a Jewish boy at age 13, when he reaches the age of religious responsibility

BERACHAH, BERACHOTH: blessing(s) said over food, new clothes, etc.

BEITH HAMIKDASH: the Holy Temple

BNEI NOACH: (literally, the sons of Noah) gentiles

BRITH MILAH: circumcision

CHASSID, CHASSIDIM: follower(s) of the chassiduth movement

CHASSIDUTH: a movement founded by the Baal Shem Tov in the sixteenth century, based on mysticism and devout observance

CHEDER: school of Torah learning for young boys

ERETZ YISRAEL: the Land of Israel

GEMARA: the commentary on the Mishnah forming the second part of the Talmud

GOYIM: gentiles

HAMASKIL: the "enlightened" — a member of the Haskalah movement, an eighteenth century movement which attempted to spread "modern" secular culture among Jews

KADDISH: the prayer recited in memory of the dead, sanctifying God's name

KEN: yes

KIBBUTZ, KIBBUTZIM: communal settlement(s)

KIDDUSH HASHEM: martyrdom

KOTHEL HAMA'ARAVI: the Western Wall

LANDSLEIT: people who come from the same home town

MASHIACH: the Messiah

MAZAL TOV: congratulations

MITZVOTH: commandments

MOSHAV, MOSHAVIM: communal farm(s)

OL MALCHUTH SHAMAYIM: the obligation to serve God

PEYOTH: ritual sidelocks of hair

REBBE: head of a chassidic group

SHABBATH: the Sabbath

SHEMA YISRAEL: the declaration of belief in one God, said twice daily and before going to sleep at night

SHEMONEH ESREH: the "Eighteen Benedictions" — the main section of the daily prayers

TALLITH: prayer shawl

TALMID CHACHAM: a scholar

TEFILLIN: two small, square, leather boxes containing parchments inscribed with passages from the Torah which are worn on the left arm and forehead of Jewish males during morning workday prayers

VIDUY: confession

YESHIVA, YESHIVOTH: talmudical school(s)

STUDY GUIDE: THE TWINS

prepared by Yitzchak Kasnett, M.S.

Chapter 1

REMEMBER THE FACTS:

1. List the characters in chapter 1 in their order of appearance.
2. List the characters according to their relationship to one another by drawing a family tree.
3. Who was kaiser of Austria when Yudel's father was in the army? During which war? Approximately what year?
4. How old is Yudel now?
5. What was the name of the town in our story?
6. Which teaching of the Rabbis did the teacher say Yudel was trying to disprove? How did Yudel answer? Was the teacher satisfied?

THINK – DISCUSS – WRITE:

Answer the following questions separately or include all your answers in one composition.

1. Describe Yudel's childhood.
2. List the positive and negative effects his childhood might have had on him.
3. Would such a childhood help or hurt a person? How or why?
4. How do you think such a childhood would have changed you?

LANGUAGE AND VOCABULARY:

1. SIMILES: The author uses a **simile** to describe the twins. A **simile** is a figure of speech that uses "like"

or "as" when comparing things. Figures of speech are phrases used like adjectives and adverbs to describe a person, place, thing or action with a colorful expression. What simile does the author use? Work with another student to think up ten more examples such as "light as a feather," "felt like two cents," "drank like a fish," "as sweet as honey."

2. PREFIXES AND SUFFIXES: Study the meanings and spellings of the following vocabulary words from the chapter:
    — ordinary
    — obvious
    — unique
    — patiently - How many meanings does the root word *patient* have? The suffix *ly* is an adverbial suffix that describes how or in what way something was done.
    — enthusiastic - The root word here is "enthuse" which is a verb. The root was built into the noun "enthusiast" which is a person. The suffix *ast* means one who practices or does. Finally, when we add *ic*, we have turned the noun into an adjective describing the person who, in this case, acts in an excited manner.
    — financial - What is the root word here? The suffix *ial* turns the noun into an adjective which describes a noun.
    — similarity - What type of word is "similar"? A noun, verb, an adjective or something else? The suffix *ity* turns some root words into nouns.
    — resemblance - The prefix *re* means "again," the root *sembler* from Old French means "to seem

or appear," and the suffix *ance* means "quality or state." So we see that the word means "the state of appearing again."

— apparent
— imperative – The prefix *im* means "in"; the root *perare* from Latin means "command or order," and the suffix *ative* means "inclined to." So we see that the word means "inclined to command."

3. KEEPING A CHART: Now that you have been introduced to the three parts of a word: the prefix, the root, and the suffix, keep a cumulative list of all new prefixes, roots, and suffixes that you encounter in the vocabulary words that are presented with each chapter. A chart for doing so will be provided by your teacher. A good advanced dictionary will not only define words for you, but give you their roots as well. Your teacher will provide you with lists of prefixes and suffixes. Your teacher will also provide you with a chart to list your vocabulary words and check off your mastery of their meanings and spellings.

Chapter 2

REMEMBER THE FACTS:

1. In what year did the Germans invade Poland?
2. How long were the Jews given to arrive at the ghetto?

3. What was the punishment for not reporting to the ghetto on time?
4. Where did Esther teach?
5. What is the real reason Yudel's father-in-law did not move into the ghetto? (See last paragraph on p. 14.)
6. Why was money so important in the ghetto?
7. How did the twins save Esther?

THINK — DISCUSS — WRITE:

1. In the second paragraph on p. 14 the author contrasts the living conditions of the poor with the wealthy. Answer the following questions in view of the situation in the novel:
   a. Did the poor really have less to lose?
   b. Why did the death threat impress the poor more?
   c. Why were some of the wealthy more concerned with their money than others who also had money?
   d. Why were the wealthy not as meek as the poor? Do poor people have to be meek? Is it a noble virtue?
2. Was it a good idea for Reb Reichman to wait and see if he would have to move into the ghetto? Does the fact that "our Sages said that an evil decree is made to be abolished" mean that he did not have to obey?
3. Would you have trusted Maria? Consider the situation carefully.
4. When the author says, "The whole world seems to revolve around a loaf of bread," how does that apply to a person who is spiritually weak? How does it apply to a spiritually strong person?

5. What could not be stolen from Yudel and Esther? Why?
6. How could one fall into despair without Torah?
7. Why did Esther take Brachah with her to teach?
8. Why was it "better to be silent than to speak in a quaking voice"?
9. The author says that it may have been a mistake for Esther to have moved and placed herself between the enemy and her students. Would you have acted differently? If so, how and why?
10. What does this statement mean: "If honest people couldn't differentiate between Brachah and Chaim, how could a person whose sight was distorted by evil tell the difference between them?"
11. Describe Esther as if she were your next-door neighbor. How would she act? What would her interests be? What kind of mother, friend or teacher would she be? Describe her as a person you know well, based on what you know about her from this chapter.

VOCABULARY:

Study the meanings and spellings of the following vocabulary words from the chapter:

- meek
- announced
- mobile
- impression
- circumstances
- encourage
- intelligent
- audience

Chapter 3

REMEMBER THE FACTS:

1. What is a parasite? Who were considered parasites and why?
2. Why did the Nazis feel that those who could not benefit them should not live?
3. What is "perpetual fear"? How can it affect a person?
4. What did the Nazis start to do to the Jews? How?
5. What were the living conditions like in the ghetto? How did people manage to exist?
6. What was the mood of the people in the ghetto?
7. How did the twins save their parents a second time?

THINK — DISCUSS — WRITE:

1. How did Yudel and Esther's view about helping people (as seen in the first paragraph on p. 23) differ from that of the Nazis' attitude (as seen in the first paragraph on p. 22)? Give some reasons why people can have such different attitudes.
2. Why was Yudel able to be "no more anxious than those who possessed the much coveted card"?
3. The author says those without work cards were "like fish caught in a net." How does one feel if he is caught in a net? How does he act?
4. In the second paragraph on p. 24, the author describes the terrible tension which everyone experienced during the "round-ups." He writes that "...people have an inborn will to live." What is this

230

inborn will? Explain and give examples. Why do people anticipate that things will get better?

5. Why did Yudel "lock his compassion in his heart"? What does this mean?

6. Read through the following questions and answer them in one composition. Be sure to include all of these issues in the composition since they are all related. What type of marriage did Yudel and Esther have? Were they good to each other? Had they become better people because of their hardships? Why can hardships and sacrifice make a person stronger or greater? Can we learn anything from this for ourselves?

LANGUAGE AND VOCABULARY:

1. A **metaphor** is a figure of speech that compares two things, but does not use the words "like" or "as." Metaphors are not meant literally, but only as an expression. The author uses the **metaphor**, "The angel of death had a thousand eyes." What does "a thousand eyes" mean here? Other examples of metaphors are "her heart is a fountain of kindness" and "Chaim is a walking dictionary."

2. Study the meanings and spellings of the following vocabulary words from the chapter:
   — precious
   — despondently
   — consequences
   — degraded
   — loath
   — parasites
   — superfluous
   — perpetual

Chapter 4

REMEMBER THE FACTS:

1. What is an apostate?
2. What was the Jewish "emancipation"?
3. What is a *maskil*?
4. What does it mean that Shimon was one of the "enlightened"?
5. What was Yaakov's conflict after he graduated from the university? How did he resolve it?
6. Whom did Yaakov marry?
7. What was Yaakov's reward for converting?
8. Did Yaakov's conversion help him? What happened?
9. What was Yaakov's personal conflict in the ghetto? How did he adjust?

THINK — DISCUSS — WRITE:

1. Why were Shimon's thoughts about Jews and gentiles "opening their hearts to one another" incorrect, even if he did believe in the teaching, *tafastah merubeh — lo tafastah*?
2. How might a Jew express his patriotism? What do our Sages say about patriotism?
3. Is it worse for someone to show that he hates you, or for him to hide his hatred and pretend that he likes you?
4. What was the final result of all the great plans Shimon had for Jews to be like gentiles? What should people like Yaakov have learned in the ghetto?

232

5. In what different ways did Yudel and Yaakov cope with their hardships?

VOCABULARY:

1. Study the meanings and spellings of the following vocabulary words from the chapter:

- —desist(ed)
- —exclaimed
- —patience
- —Gymnasium
- —hindrance
- —existence
- —inheritance
- —decisive

Chapter 5

REMEMBER THE FACTS:

1. Why did Esther change the place where she taught?
2. How old were the girls in Esther's second class?
3. How did Esther respond to the needs of her students academically, emotionally and physically?
4. How long had the Jews lived in Poland?
5. What was wrong with Marussa?

THINK — DISCUSS — WRITE:

1. How was there "hope" in the fact that "history was repeating itself"?

2. What lesson do we learn from Chava and her parents?

3. On p. 41, the last sentence in the second paragraph talks about the Poles and Germans. What does this teach us about gentile nations, their relationships among themselves and with the Jews? Where else in history do we find a similar situation which teaches us *ma'aseh avos siman levanim* — what happens to the fathers, eventually happens to the children"?

VOCABULARY:

1. Study the meanings and spellings of the following vocabulary words from the chapter:

   —liable
   —intermingled
   —ensnare
   —heroines
   —engrossed
   —collaborated

Chapter 6

REMEMBER THE FACTS:

1. At what time and where was the line-up?
2. Why was Marussa ashamed?
3. What was the reason for the line-up?
4. What was Esther's decision in the square?

THINK — DISCUSS — WRITE:

1. How could Chaim's "fear be as great as the adults," when he was only a little boy? What does this teach us about children and how one needs to act in their presence?

2. Why was it that Esther could "not allow herself to waiver," and that "any slight hesitation might spoil everything?"

3. What did Yudel learn from his childhood that helped him understand Esther, her relationship to her girls, and her service to Hashem — something that caused him to pull his hand back and completely overrule every natural feeling and instinct that he might have had?

4. Outline the decisions and deeds that Esther and Yudel had performed in the ghetto which allowed them, now, together, to act on such an exalted level. Show how these decisions and deeds affected and shaped them. Try to list one or two important incidents in your own life and how they substantially changed how you now think or live.

5. What kind of courage did Esther instill in her students? How? What did she represent to them?

6. How must one view the world in order to be willing to die for a mitzvah?

7. Why is the simile, "as white as shrouds," used so effectively?

8. Why did the girls feel that the seeds gave them a victory over their enemies? Weren't they captives? Captives of whom? What are the real enemies who capture and imprison us?

9. Explain the phrase "a tremor of holiness."

10. Describe how you would feel if you were Esther.
    What sense of responsibility, devotion and love for
    your fellow Jew would you have? What would your
    feelings be towards Hashem? Or, describe how you
    would feel if you were one of the girls on the train.
    Create the dialogue, the feelings, the thoughts the
    girls might have had during this, their last train
    ride? What would they talk about? How would they
    feel about each other, their parents, their Creator?

VOCABULARY:

Study the meanings and spellings of the following words
from the chapter:

> —emitted
> —muster
> —impatient
> —sufficient
> —courageous
> —caressed
> —tremor
> —tranquility
> —cudgel
> —deportation

Chapter 7

REMEMBER THE FACTS:

1. Who was Mr. Sokolsky?
2. What was his son's name?

3. What made him change his mind about the Jews?
    What was his "tragedy"?
4. How were Mr. and Mrs. Sokolsky treated differently
    from their son?
5. What does it mean to say, "a drowning man will
    clutch at any straw"?

THINK — DISCUSS — WRITE:

In this chapter, three different types of literary
techniques are used by the author:
> Irony
> Stereotyping
> Propagandizing

Irony is an outcome of events contrary to what might
have been expected. For example, a highly industrious,
hard working man with many debts, is in desperate need
of a job. After much searching, he finally finds work as
a salesman, but the job offers a low salary with long
hours. The man's next-door neighbor is also looking for
a job. The neighbor is quite well off, has no debts, and is
a rather lazy individual who does not like to work too
hard. He also finds a sales job, but *his* job has shorter
hours and pays a very good salary.

Stereotyping is the designation or conception of a large
group of people as having a common characteristic
regardless of the fact that some, or even many members of
the group do not have this characteristic. For example: All
people who live in that town are nasty.

1. Find at least five statements in this chapter that are
    examples of stereotyping. When answering the

following two questions (numbers 2 and 3), give special thought to the many ways in which the Jews have been stereotyped throughout history, and how ironic these stereotypes have actually been.

2. "They are all liars," Stashek said. "The Jews are a strange people. It's no wonder that the Poles don't love them." Why was this so ironical?

3. How did the gentiles reinforce their opinion that the Jews were a filthy people? What was the irony in this opinion?

Propagandizing, the third of the literary techniques introduced in this chapter, is the systematic promotion of a particular idea to further one's own cause and usually to damage an opposing one. It is the twisting of public opinion to conform to your point of view by presenting only the information you wish to present, and in the manner you wish to present it.

For example, a legislator wishes to vote down a suggestion for a new municipal sales tax to pay for a water purification plant. He explains that the sales tax will result in people shopping in a neighboring town where there is no tax, and that the resultant loss in sales will force the city's stores to fire workers, causing the city to pay out large sums in unemployment compensation.

The legislator does not mention, however, that the water which the people in the city are drinking is dangerously polluted, and that the new plant is absolutely vital to the health and welfare of the people; that building and running the new plant will result in many new jobs; that the neighboring town will buy water from the new plant, thus guaranteeing a nice profit; and that if the sales tax is not passed, the city will simply have to find some other way of taxing its citizens in order to finance the plant.

By presenting only one side of the story, the legislator is distorting the picture. He is propagandizing.

4. Research some of the common vicious, anti-Semitic propaganda that the Germans used to depict the Jews. How did they distort and undermine the holiness of Hashem's people?

VOCABULARY:

Study the meanings and spellings of the following words from the chapter:

- perplexed
- derision
- dignity
- disparagingly
- noncommittal
- indifferent
- ridicule
- obscure

Chapter 8

REMEMBER THE FACTS:

1. Why didn't Yudel go home? Why didn't he go to bring Brachah with him?
2. Who is Shimon? What is he like?
3. Why did Shimon receive a grade-A work card?
4. Who is Zechariah?
5. Where did Shimon have his meeting?
6. Who is Mr. Shefler?

THINK — DISCUSS — WRITE:

1. Why was it that Yudel could find no peace of mind? How is this a *ma'aseh avos siman levanim*?
2. What secret did Yudel have which enabled him to bear his suffering about Esther and Brachah?
3. Why was Yudel worried about Brachah finding her place again amongst the Jews?
4. Do you agree with Shimon's philosophy about fighting back? Is this a Torah-true attitude? (See last paragraph on p. 64 to top of p. 65)
5. What was the group's plan for escape? Was it a wise one? Could it endanger those who remained in the ghetto? Who should the group have spoken to before they acted? What would have been your thoughts and actions? What considerations would you have made? Be comprehensive in listing the pros and cons of each plan, or part of each plan you develop. Perhaps you could join with a few other students and devise your plan as a group.

240

VOCABULARY:

Study the meanings and spellings of the following words
from the chapter:

- —hooligans
- —extinguish
- —esteem
- —aroused
- —dexterous
- —immersed
- —expropriated
- —heartily

Chapter 9

REMEMBER THE FACTS:

1. Where was Brachah?
2. How did she feel about being there?
3. Where were the other girls from?

THINK — DISCUSS — WRITE:

1. On p. 70 Brachah realizes that Chaim, and not she,
   is with her parents. She has been placed in strange
   new surroundings for the third time — first in the
   ghetto; then with Marussa; and now in the convent.
   How could such changes affect her emotional and
   mental growth? How do such experiences shape the
   way one feels and thinks? Do they make us fearful,
   confident or shy? Honest or dishonest? Open with
   others, or closed and suspicious? What are the

emotional and psychological effects that these
upheavals might have had on Brachah?

2. How would Maria's disapproval make Brachah feel
   about herself? How did this shape her behavior?
3. Why did Brachah like the fact that all the women
   were dressed the same way? What did this convey to
   her?
4. What does the nuns' belief in "Jewish magic" reveal
   about the attitude of the Christians towards the
   Jewish religion?

VOCABULARY:

Study the meanings and spellings of the following words
from the chapter:
- verge
- legible
- perplexed

Chapter 10

REMEMBER THE FACTS:

1. Which forest did the Jews escape to?
2. Jews from another ghetto joined the Jews of
   Nachrovah in the forest. What was the name of that
   ghetto?
3. What did Shimon and Peretz have in common?
4. Describe Peretz. How do you view him?
5. We have been introduced to several new characters.
   Update your character list by charting all of the
   characters in order of their appearance.

6. What did Shimon and Peretz do for the Jewish partisans as soon as they arrived in the forest?
7. How did the Jews get food in the forest?
8. What does the word "seat" mean in the second to last line on p. 79?

THINK — DISCUSS — WRITE:

1. Why did Yudel volunteer? He knew he could be killed and he knew Esther had probably killed herself to sanctify the name of Hashem. What did he think would happen to his children? Did he act responsibly? What would you have done?
2. Was Yudel really dreaming? Or was he overwhelmed by the events of the recent past which he had been trying to forget? Have you ever had a similar experience?

VOCABULARY:

Study the meanings and spellings of the following words from the chapter:

- betray
- partisans
- authorities
- enforce
- cunning
- precious
- suspicion
- eligible
- dispossessed

Chapter 11

REMEMBER THE FACTS:

1. How were the nuns treating Brachah? Why? How did her friends react?
2. How did Brachah protect herself from the new "treatment"?
3. What contradiction did Marussa see in the church?
4. How did Marussa's status change?
5. What caused Marussa to visit the convent?

THINK — DISCUSS — WRITE:

1. How did Brachah know her father was nearby? Was Brachah's dream just a coincidence? Or was the author trying to keep the reader's imagination working?
2. Why did Brachah change, and how did Marussa's visit change her? What did Marussa now represent to Brachah?

VOCABULARY:

Study the meanings and spellings of the following words from the chapter:

> — mystifying
> — admiration
> — explicitly
> — heroine
> — shunned
> — heresy

Chapter 12

REMEMBER THE FACTS:

1. When was the last time Chaim saw Brachah?
2. What dreams does Chaim have about Brachah?
3. How did Shimon's assigning guard duty to Chaim help the child?
4. How is the earth "an ally of the oppressed"?

THINK — DISCUSS — WRITE:

1. Why was Chaim jealous of Brachah?
2. How could living in such an isolated situation as the forest change a person? How might he feel about himself and others if he were living so far away from a normal community? What are some positive changes, and what might some negative ones be? How would you respond in such a situation?
3. What does Brachah's behavior in the dream tell us about her now?

VOCABULARY:

Study the meanings and spellings of the following words from the chapter:
> — assumed
> — dominate
> — innovator

— exploit
— sufficient
— curiosity
— muse
— reveries
— suspicious

Chapter 13

REMEMBER THE FACTS:

1. What new reason did the Poles have to hate the Jews?
2. Why was Stashek more at ease?
3. What similarity do we see between the Poles and the Germans during their confrontation in the forest?
4. Who was the Poles' commander?

VOCABULARY:

Study the meanings and spellings of the following words from the chapter:

— deriding
— leisurely
— jubilance
— complacency
— imminent
— collaborated
— ruckus
— benevolently

Chapter 14

REMEMBER THE FACTS:

1. What was most convenient for the partisans? Why?
2. What was dear to the Poles?
3. What mutual plan of action did the Jews and Poles plot together?
4. What are the reasons Shimon chose Paltiel for the first mission?
5. What kind of person was Paltiel?

THINK — DISCUSS — WRITE:

1. If you were Shimon, how would you feel about sharing a camp with the Poles after Paltiel did not return? What would you think? How would you plan for the safety of your group?

VOCABULARY:

Study the meanings and spellings of the following words from the chapter:

- exploits
- convenient

Chapter 15

REMEMBER THE FACTS:

1. How did the farmers feel about the train incident?

2. How was Paltiel's death avenged?
3. What confrontation occurred between the two groups? Why? What insight does this give us regarding the personality of the Poles?
4. What new event was happening on the eastern front?

THINK — DISCUSS — WRITE:

1. How does the first paragraph describe the major, basic difference in the values of the Jews and the Poles?
2. What is the irony in Shimon's thought: "The price of Jewish honor is very high. Only by dying can a Jew gain esteem." How does a Jew normally achieve "honor" in Jewish eyes — by dying or through living? What does this reveal regarding the Poles' understanding of living in a holy way?
3. Explain the statement: "Anger needs no logical justification. It is always justified in its own eyes." Have you ever been angry? Have you allowed this anger, logical or not, to justify how you thought and acted, as if an entirely new set of rules for behavior had just been invented? Can you describe one or more incidents when this happened to you? Do you now have any new insights about anger?

VOCABULARY:

Study the meanings and spellings of the following words from the chapter:

> — rancor
> — befitting

Chapter 16

REMEMBER THE FACTS:

1. What was the reaction of the partisans to the German retreat?
2. What was the state of mind of the Germans?
3. What stereotyped image of the Jews did the Nazis teach to the German soldiers? How does this stereotype distort and destroy the concept of the Jewish value of life?

THINK — DISCUSS — WRITE:

How did Shimon and Vachek differ regarding the killing of the German? What fundamental differences in morality and values does this express? Compare these differences to the differences in values between Yaakov and Esav.

VOCABULARY:

Study the meanings and spellings of the following words from the chapter:
— subjugation
— self-assured

Chapter 17

REMEMBER THE FACTS:

1. What did the Jews find in the ghetto after leaving the forest? How had the Poles acted?
2. How did Stashek treat Shimon and Peretz?
3. What was the situation in Temyonovah?
4. What were the thoughts and emotions of the Jews at the cemetery?

THINK — DISCUSS — WRITE:

1. What was the Jews' attitude towards death? Did they consider death "final"? How did they sanctify it? How did they find comfort in their attitude towards death?
2. If you had been at the cemetery that day how would you have reacted? What would you have felt? What would your thoughts have been? Try to record them as if you were there, preserving the experience in your diary.

VOCABULARY:

Study the meanings and spellings of the following words from the chapter:
—noncommittal
—quizzically

Chapter 18

REMEMBER THE FACTS:

1. Why were the Poles on the train so bitter?
2. Why was there a heavy silence in the train car?
3. What happened to the train on the way to Cracow?
4. Why did Peretz and Yonah choose to immigrate to Israel?

THINK — DISCUSS — WRITE:

Write a eulogy for Shimon. What would you say to memorialize what this man had done for the Jews under his protection and what he meant to them?

VOCABULARY:

Study the meanings and spellings of the following words from the chapter:

— contempt
— enmity
— efficiently
— adjacent
— preferential

Chapter 19

REMEMBER THE FACTS:

1. What incident occurred in the yard of the convent?
2. What was Brachah's new name?

THINK — DISCUSS — WRITE:

1. What ploy or stratagem were the nuns using to brainwash the girls by letting them walk through the ghetto, particularly now that the war was over and the ghetto was empty? What message was this conveying to the girls about the Jews?
2. What incident reveals that the nuns were becoming successful with Brachah?

VOCABULARY:

Study the meanings and spellings of the following words from the chapter:
- indignantly
- obliterate
- exclamations

Chapter 20

REMEMBER THE FACTS:

1. Where was Chaim placed in Israel?
2. Why did Chaim study so hard?
3. How did the intensity of Chaim's feelings for Brachah change as he grew older?

THINK — DISCUSS — WRITE:

1. Why is diligence a trait that is to be highly esteemed? What do we know about diligence regarding the learning of Torah?
2. Why was Chaim convinced that Brachah would remain a true Jew? What was the basis for his reasoning?

VOCABULARY:

Study the meanings and spellings of the following words from the chapter:
- diligence
- astute
- refuge

Chapter 21

REMEMBER THE FACTS:

1. How had Brachah fared in her relationship with the Church?

2. How did Sarah react to the request that she return to Judaism?
3. What was Brachah's new family name?
4. Why did the emergence of the new State of Israel trouble the priests and monks?
5. What scheme did the priests devise to convert Jews living in the Holy Land?
6. What troubled Marussa about Barbara's new position in the Holy Land?
7. Why was Barbara jealous of Yanka?

THINK — DISCUSS — WRITE:

1. What was decided concerning Brachah now that she had completed the Catholic seminary? Why? Explain in detail.
2. What was the plight of the Jews left wandering in Eastern Europe?
3. How was Barbara able to tip the scales in favor of the Church when she confronted these people?
4. The priests felt that "sinful thoughts are the greatest sin of all." How did the priests wield this view over the masses throughout the ages? What is the Torah viewpoint on the subject of thinking about forbidden things? Explain your answer in full detail, and if necessary refer to appropriate source material.

VOCABULARY:

Study the meanings and spellings of the following words from the chapter:

— absolution

—heretic
—sustenance
—apprehensive
—emigrating

Chapter 22

THINK — DISCUSS — WRITE:

1. What had so startled Barbara on her first walk in
   Jerusalem with Paulina? Why? What relationship
   did it have to her dreams that night?
2. Why were Barbara's emotions a sign of weakness?
   What was the nature of her internal struggle? Have
   you ever been in a situation where, although your
   logic pointed in one direction, your feelings and
   emotions pulled you in another? Try to explain how
   you felt, and how Barbara must have felt.

VOCABULARY:

Study the meanings and spellings of the following words
from the chapter:
           —preoccupied
           —relinquish
           —melodious
           —bewildered
           —novelty
           —emanating

Chapter 23

REMEMBER THE FACTS:

1. What happened to the Jews of Nachrovah?
2. Why had more Jews been killed in Poland than in Germany?
3. How did the preparation for aliyah help the Jews?
4. How did Peretz spend his time upon arriving in Israel?

THINK — DISCUSS — WRITE:

1. What was the British Mandate in Palestine?
2. How did the ingathering of Jews in Cracow from their various places of banishment during the war affect them? How did they relate to each other? Pick one of the experiences mentioned in the chapter and imagine yourself as the storyteller. Can you? Do you believe what you are saying is really true, or just a nightmare?
3. Why did some Jews want to remain in Poland and Germany? Explore the possible emotional and psychological reasons for this. Why did the author write that they remained "for reasons beyond our comprehension" (top of p. 170)?
4. What did Peretz mean when he said, "How wonderful that in Eretz Yisroel even the goyim are Jewish"? What does this statement mean to you? How does it make you feel?

256

VOCABULARY:

Study the meanings and spellings of the following words
from the chapter:
- excursions
- immigrate
- abducted

Chapter 24

REMEMBER THE FACTS:

1. Why were the Jews of Nachrovah saddened after
being given their own homes?
2. What date was chosen for the annual convention of
Nachrovah Jews? Why?
3. What had happened to Yaakov Shimeonowitz during
the war? What was his present dilemma and why did
he finally show up at one of the conventions?

THINK — DISCUSS — WRITE:

1. Are you surprised that Marussa still loved Yank and
wished to rejoin him? What does the fact that Yanka
was so curious to see her father tell you about
Marussa? If we study Marussa carefully we find that
she is a character of conflict and contradiction, that
she is very tentative and insecure in her decisions
and feelings. Why is this? What type of person is she
in your eyes? What is the nature of her conflict?

VOCABULARY:

Study the meanings and spellings of the following words from the chapter:

- queried
- incidentally
- elicited

Chapter 25

REMEMBER THE FACTS:

1. What was the sole criterion for Marcus's immigration to Israel?
2. How did Marcus react to living in Israel?

THINK — DISCUSS — WRITE:

What is the significance of the title "Pan"?

VOCABULARY:

Study the meanings and spellings of the following words from the chapter:

- agitator
- disillusioned
- conscience
- lenient
- sufficed
- curiosity

Chapter 26

REMEMBER THE FACTS:

1. How did Marcus react to the Judean Hills on his trip to Jerusalem? How was he affected by the trip?

THINK — DISCUSS — WRITE:

1. How do you feel about Marcus as a character? Describe his personality in terms of his world outlook and his great sense of dignity and truth. How do these character traits interact in his personality? What meaning do they have for him?
2. How did Marcus let Barbara rationalize away his apprehension while enrolling his daughters in the Mission school?

VOCABULARY:

Study the meanings and spellings of the following words from the chapter:

- allayed
- anxiety
- affirmation
- hastily
- hesitantly
- enticements
- apparently
- astonishment
- icon

Chapter 27

REMEMBER THE FACTS:

1. Why was Marussa hesitant about revealing the information she knew about Barbara? What was her conflict? Where was her allegiance?
2. How did the townspeople view Marussa now?
3. Why was Marussa suffering such terrible tension? What personal adjustments does one make in order to function under stress?

THINK — DISCUSS — WRITE:

The Jews in Israel did not fit Marussa's stereotyped picture of Jews as she knew them. Why weren't the Jews farmers in Europe during the last five or six hundred years or more? What kind of laws were made against Jews and how did these laws dictate the ways a Jew could earn a living during these times?

VOCABULARY:

Study the meanings and spellings of the following words from the chapter:

- sympathize
- disconcerted
- ridicule
- scorn
- enviable

Chapter 28

REMEMBER THE FACTS:

What type of person is Rosa? Is she a woman of deep or strong convictions?

THINK — DISCUSS — WRITE:

1. Why did the Judean Hills lose their magic for Marcus? How do they represent some aspect of the yearning of the Jewish soul?
2. Chaim's meeting with Marcus and Rosa was obviously an open exhibition of Divine Providence. Has any incident like this ever happened to you? What insights do incidents like these give us about the world and the way it is run?

VOCABULARY:

Study the meanings and spellings of the following words from the chapter:
—preoccupied
—Inquisition

Chapter 29

REMEMBER THE FACTS:

1. What avenues of action did the *yeshivah* students at the assembly suggest as possible methods to fight the Mission?

2. What course of action did the assembly choose? Did their plan work? Was the public rallied to their side? Why or why not?
3. Why did the Mission not inform the police of Barbara's disappearance?

THINK — DISCUSS — WRITE:

What does the saying of the Sages "All Jews are responsible for each other" mean to us in our daily lives? How does it guide us in our behavior towards others? How is it reflected in the course of our novel? Explain in detail.

VOCABULARY:

Study the meanings and spellings of the following words from the chapter:
- infiltrating
- sentiment
- proselytize
- disconcerting
- unscrupulous
- devious

Chapter 30

REMEMBER THE FACTS:

1. Marussa and Yanka had their names changed. What were their new names?
2. What was the source of David's grief?

THINK — DISCUSS — WRITE:

1. Describe your distress if your brother or sister had been abducted by the Church, baptized, and brought up as a gentile.
2. Today, tens of thousands of Jews are being "lost" as a result of assimilation. Describe your own thoughts and feelings concerning this matter. How aware of, or concerned about it, are you? Do you feel any measure of responsibility? Does this lead to any active steps on your part?

VOCABULARY:

Study the meanings and spellings of the following words from the chapter:
- revive
- edict
- glimmer

Other Feldheim novels
by BenZion Firer

THE LONG JOURNEY HOME

Shlomo, a brilliant, young talmudic student, and Zissel, the daughter of a wealthy, assimilated family, both leave Poland to become pioneers in Palestine. The Promised Land, however, is a disappointing whirlwind of conflicting Zionist ideologies. Shlomo, in his non-ending search for a just society, journeys to the communist "utopia" of Russia. Zissel also returns to Europe, and both of them, caught up in the horrors of World War II, attempt to find meaning in their existence as Jews. A fascinating story of a confusing and complex era in recent Jewish history. Translated by Bracha Slae.

SAADIAH WEISSMAN

The thousands of Yemenite Jews who came to the Holy Land in 1948 were confronted with a strange and frightening 20th century world. When hundreds of their children suddenly vanished, rumors persisted that they had been abducted and sent to non-observant families and kibbutzim who would integrate them into the life of modern Israel. *Saadiah Weissman* is the story of one such child whose two "families" become tragically intermingled.
An absorbing novel which chronicles the first tumultuous twenty years of the fledgling State of Israel, its conflicts, problems and challenges. Translated by Chava Shulman.